Heart of ﹢

Bri Woodall
Di   07960 854447

Heart of a Cyclist

A TRUE STORY OF SURVIVAL AND RECOVERY

John Evans

YouCaxton Publications
Oxford & Shrewsbury

For Stephanie and Kelly, my two greatest achievements in life, you are the best part of me.

For Riley-John, Freya-Marie, Isla-Rose, Esmie-Grace, live your lives to the full, believe in yourselves always, follow your hearts, chase your dreams, anything is possible.

For my Dad, you gave me the tools, the strength, the fire deep inside - until we meet again.

Epigraph

The Ventoux is a god of evil, to which sacrifices must be made. It never forgives weakness and extracts an unfair tribute of suffering.

Physically, the Ventoux is dreadful. Bald, it's the spirit of dry, its climate makes it a damned terrain, a testing place for heroes, something like a higher hell.

Roland Barthes.
French philosopher and bicycle-racing fan.

Contents

Acknowledgements

I make my apologies now for anyone I fail to mention by name, there are so many good people who helped and supported me in many different ways on this journey. I appreciate everything that was done for me so much. None of this would have been possible without you, thank you all.

Mr & Mrs B for convincing me that maybe I had a story worth telling. Without your encouragement I don't think this story would have ever been written. I thank you both sincerely for the push I needed.

Dr Barr, without his initial intervention and critical care I would undoubtedly have not survived the MI. I will be forever grateful to him and all the amazing Nurses, Doctors, and staff at the Coronary care department within Russells-Hall Hospital. All the Nurses and staff in both the ICU & Coronary care departments at New Cross Hospital, without them I would not have made it through those dark days, no thanks could ever be enough.

To everyone at Action Heart, the year I spent there was one of my best years. I am grateful for having met so many wonderful people, it was an honour and a privilege to spend my rehabilitation in such good company, being cared for in such a fantastic way. I wish you all good health always, thank you.

Ioanna Alexiou, my long suffering sports-and-exercise physiologist, I thank you for your endless patience and willingness to help me change and adapt my approach towards training. Without your input I would have burned out and most likely done myself some real damage. Working with me to control the inner chimp was never going to be easy or pretty but I feel we got there in the end. I am honored you took the time to write the foreword for this journey in which you played a big part. My sincere thanks, I couldn't have done it without you. Keep bouncing that ball.

To all my friends both in and out of brigade who came to visit me by the truck-load during my time in the hospitals, your constant support was so much appreciated and very humbling in the extreme, it meant a lot to me then as it does now, stay strong, be safe.

Pat, Richie and the boys for turning out on that cold, wet, windy October morning to support me getting back on the bike for the first time, sorry for dragging us up camp hill, keep em turning boys.

Pat at the Spider's Web for keeping us well fed and watered, always a pleasure.

To all at The Shrewsbury Coffee House for the pastries, panini, wonderful coffees and always washing and refilling our bottles, very much appreciated.

My dear friend Liz Fox for tolerating my endless cycling tales and talk of the Ventoux, the flapjacks kept us well fueled right to the top, thank you.

My family, I thank you for your support and for tolerating my frustrations and single-minded focus throughout that whole year, you were there for me on the good days but, more importantly, on all of the bad ones too. I can only apologize for putting you all through what must have been hell, but we made it back together. I love you all deeply for it, thank you is not enough.

Mr Matuszewski, without you sir I would simply not be here today. You gave back to me the gift which is my life. You gave me the belief and motivation to get back on my feet and push on. In my opinion, you performed nothing short of a miracle with your skills and dedication, no words or amount of thanks on my part could come close to what I owe you and your team. I only hope you may feel some pride in knowing that your amazing efforts and extraordinary skills, the time you invested in doing your best to save me, have not been wasted. God bless you sir.

My band of brothers, Big George, Paul, Digger, Stig, I couldn't have made that climb without you, I am proud of you all for the ride you put in that day, the sacrifices you made, the efforts you put in to get there and support me. It was a big ask. I will always appreciate it and treasure the memories of our climb up the Ventoux. It was an honour and a privilege to share the road and ride with you. I genuinely thank you all.

Big George, you rode with me through thick and thin, come hell or high water. I could never have come back as strong as I did without your constant support, your journey was equal to mine, chapeaux sir, we had a good year, forever in your debt.

Mr Fowke and everyone at YouCaxton.co.uk thank you for your support, guidance and professionalism, turning my story into the finished book it has become. I most certainly could not have done this without you.

Foreword

By Ioanna Alexiou.

Meeting new patients at a cardiovascular rehabilitation clinic is for me a daily occurrence. Every patient is very different with their own individual needs. During my career I have encountered patients who required a lot of encouragement to undertake their exercise regime, patients who enjoyed the social side of the of the clinic far more than the actual exercise, also patients who pushed themselves far more than suggested to them.

That is exactly how I first met John. He was one of the patients you could put into the third category plus some more. He never missed a training session for the whole year of his rehabilitation program. Every session he would push himself trying to do more than the session before even if it were fifty-one push-ups instead of fifty. He would not rest until he had done so. Of course, all this completely against our protocols.

Experience has taught me to keep a close eye on such patients but John was a one-off from the start. I had the, shall we say challenging, job of overlooking John's progress over the months, trying my best to make sure he would not overdo things with his exercise volume. Many times, we discussed his overall activity including the days he would exercise outside of the clinic. I remember trying to find the best way to tell him to take things a little easier. I did not want to discourage him as I could see John was a patient who needed a lot of self-motivation to get back on his feet after a major heart event.

As part of being a clinical sports and exercise physiologist, my role involves creating a safe environment for exercise, educating the patients on secondary prevention, regularly assessing the patient's fitness, health and lifestyle, mainly to assist in empowering them back to a normal lifestyle for each individual.

John was different in many ways. He already seemed to have a good level of knowledge in healthy living, as in nutrition, exercise and risk-factors; my main concern was that he was one of those people who pushes himself to the extreme and I imagined had always done so.

For the whole time John attended the clinic I worked with him on trying to modify his goals a little. Talking about this subject sometimes felt pointless as he did not agree with me. We would have some interesting debates. In my thoughts I maintained the belief there might be the slim chance he would listen to me.

When I first met John, it was clear for obvious reasons he was not the average seventy-year-old man that usually attends the clinic; in less than the year John spent under my care at the clinic it became obvious he was not an average forty-year-old man either. He shared his plans with me to attempt to climb Mont Ventoux on the first anniversary of his heart event or 'blip' as he called it. Most people with a similar condition are glad to return to a normal easy lifestyle and sensibly so, not train and push themselves to their limits in order to climb a mountain in just a year.

John and I became good friends and I wished him well in his quest to reach his goals, I hoped he would achieve what he set out to achieve in a safe and measured fashion, without pushing himself beyond his limits which at times I know he comes very close to. There is stubborn, driven, determined - then there is

John. Every once in a while, I find myself thinking, this job never fails to surprise me. John was one of those surprises.

Ioanna Alexiou. MSc, BSc,
Clinical exercise & sports Physiologist.

Introduction

I had half thought about the possibility of writing my story on a few occasions, but never really took the whole idea much further than just that, a passing thought, a Romantic whim in a daydream moment where I would smile to myself at the notion people might indeed be interested in what I have to say and why? The seed however was planted firmly in mind over a splendid cup of tea sat in the glorious sunshine while chatting with some dear friends of mine; we were talking generally about the ups and downs that life presents us all with over time, and how this shapes us into the people we become, and the choices and decisions we make as result. My friends began to explain to me that they, and indeed others who knew me and the events in this story, had been somewhat impressed and, dare I say it, inspired to a certain degree by my journey and the many ups and downs the whole adventure had taken me on.

The comment was made: 'you should write a book mate'. Smiling, I had explained my thoughts about the idea on numerous occasions over the past couple of years. 'Why not?' I could tell in that moment there was more than a hint of genuine intent in the comments, it got my mind to thinking seriously about the whole idea for the first time. Right there and then, sat in the sunshine with these good people, the idea was born: maybe I did have a story worth telling. I kicked ideas around in my mind for a few months and then eventually took the plunge, made a plan, and began to write what follows in these pages.

The events or to be precise the event that took place on 9th June 2013 without question changed my whole life, physically, psychologically and emotionally in every way. I would never be the same again.

My love affair and passion for cycling began from an early age; my dad would often say 'you couldn't walk properly but you could pedal a bike' and so it was the case. It was always about the bike with me, I didn't care about the weather or being alone or what bike I had to ride; I just wanted to be outside pedaling. I lived on a bike as a kid. My first bike was a hand-painted hand-me-down of my sister's but I loved it. I was allowed to ride up and down the street outside of our house, I literally wore the bike out as I did with all my bikes that followed. My boxer then grifter never owed my parents a penny, I rode them till the wheels fell off. I was about ten years old the first time I saw the Tour de France, I was hooked, completely captivated by the sport where hard men push themselves to their limits and beyond in the pursuit of glory, living in a world of pleasure and pain, such is the life of a cyclist. I was inspired by their strength, power, ability and willingness to suffer and push on through the obvious pain, striving to achieve their goals. None more so than the late and truly great Laurent Fignon, he was and still is, to this day, my inspiration in cycling.

I was fortunate to have been blessed with enough natural talent and ability to suffer, enabling me to enjoy some success on the track-cycling scene through my teenage years, as well as spending every spare minute riding on the roads, training and indeed furthering my ability to endure and suffer. I loved every minute of it and always have. Little did I know back then that this capacity to endure would be so vital to me in the struggles I would face following the events of 9th June 2013. I would be required to dig in and suffer beyond any point I imagined I could go. I believe that without cycling and what it gave me over the years, I would have been beat before I started.

In the pages that follow I will attempt to tell you my story of a journey I feel I was destined to take somehow. I have tried to tell how I saw and felt about it along the way, from the darkest of my days, staring death in the face, unsure of survival, to setting almost impossible goals, from talking to God, to my own inner demons, from the intensive coronary-care unit to the high mountains of the French alps.

The laughter and tears, the pleasure and pain, life-lessons learned, the doubts and fears, the search for motivation and belief in myself to carry me on this journey of exactly a year with all its highs and lows. It was a hell of a ride and the toughest of my life. It truly was a mountain to climb in every sense of the word.

I set out with the hope that by telling the story of my journey, I might in some small way provide some inspiration to people who are faced with their own mountains to climb whatever their circumstances and reasons, inspire them to believe in themselves even on the darkest of days when all you want to do is quit. Set yourself goals and focus on them, believe in your ability to dig in, suffer and endure, if needs be; it doesn't matter what your goals are - for me it was always going to be about the bike for sure, but it can be anything, whatever works for you, just believe in yourself. If only one person reads my story and takes inspiration from it, then my journey was not a wasted one.

For as long as God spares me, I will keep doing what I do best, pushing one pedal down after the other. Enjoy the journey, enjoy the ride.

1

The Darkest Dawn, 9th June 2013

'Can you hear me, John? Can you hear me? Squeeze my hand if you can. Hello, John you're ok, just lay still.'

This wasn't the first time in my life I had come round in a confused daze, it was the summer of 1984 and I was racing my first season on the track, a junior individual event; coming out of the last bend my chain had snapped sending me cartwheeling down the finishing straight like a rag doll. I was knocked out cold despite the helmet I was wearing, which certainly saved me as it would on many occasions during my five seasons racing on the track. The race referee and St John's Ambulance medics were gathered around me, the dust off the track filled my lungs, the horrendous burning feeling on my knees, lower back, elbows and hips told me the track had taken more than its fair share of my skin off for its duty. That is the price you must be prepared to pay for cycling in any form: pain pure and simple. You have to learn to love the pain and it's a love affair I have been involved with all my life. 1984 was a year I spent learning this love very well; that summer I had watched my childhood inspiration for getting on the bike and pedaling it as far, hard and fast as I could, the late and truly great French cyclist Laurent Fignon, win his second Tour de France. I was so inspired by his strength and endurance and the passion with which he rode that tour. I had dreamed of emulating my idol and inspiration; we all got to have dreams, right? He was sadly taken from this world far too young.

'Can you hear me, John?'

The voice came drifting back into my head again, but this was different, this was very different, there was no track dust in my mouth and no burning sensation where the skin would have been missing from parts of my body paid to the track. I was gagging, almost choking, I could feel something being pulled slowly from my throat. I could hardly breath. Unable to move, I was beginning to panic.

'Lay still, John. Hold my hand.' The calm soft voice of the nurse was with me. I felt kind of heavy; nothing wanted to move; my arms and legs were like lumps of wood as though I had ridden a hundred miler flat out and blown up; my head was banging and worst of all I couldn't see. Not a thing, just a blur of shadows and lights, I had no colour or focus. I was getting scared as confusion took over me. I had no clue where I was or what was going on; I could hear, and thank God for that, although I didn't recognize any of the many sounds or voices that surrounded me.

The soft voice spoke again: 'Lay still, John. You're ok, you're in hospital, we're taking care of you. Just lay still for now.'

I had no choice. I put my complete faith and trust in this soft, warm, comforting voice stood next to me, holding my hand, my invisible guardian angel.

The 9th June 2013 is a date which is now for ever engrained in my life as the beginning of my second chance, my privileged second bite of the cherry if you will. I was right to trust in my guardian angel. Just as she had told me it would, my sight returned slowly and my vision became clearer. My heart goes out to the people who lose their sight because, for a short while, I was afraid I had lost mine. It is a very frightening experience and I cannot begin to imagine the difficulties these people face. God bless them I say.

'I will get you some food, John. There's soup and a roll, would you like that?'

'Could I have ice cream please? I would just love some ice cream.'

I had an indescribable desire and craving for ice cream; my throat was so sore at this point and I still had no clue as to why I was in the hospital. Strange coincidence would have it that just as my vision was clearing to the point that I could see faces that were close to me, there she was, my voice, my guardian angel smiling at me with almost a cheeky grin on her face.

'How are you feeling now?' she asked. 'I've managed to find you some ice cream.'

At this point I couldn't move my arms enough to feed myself so, bless her, she sat there and spoon fed me my plain vanilla ice cream. Nothing in my life before or since has ever tasted so good, a king's ransom could not of bought the soothing, cooling, sweet ice cream from me it was simply perfection.

'The doctor will come to see you soon,' was the answer that continually greeted my ears each time I asked why I was in hospital and what had happened to me. It seemed like an age until the doctor arrived but in reality, it was no more than twenty minutes since I had regained consciousness from what turned out to be an induced coma that I had been laying in for the past three days. The doctor, or to be correct the cardiology consultant, arrived at my bedside, a wiry, lean-looking chap, I recall thinking 'he's built like a cyclist'. He smiled and introduced himself. I made the best effort I could to shake his hand; my limbs were beginning to function a little more normally by now. He explained that I had suffered a myocardial infarction on quite a large scale. To this day, I have no conscious memory of anything that occurred prior to my waking in hospital. I had received cpr, adrenaline shot, and x4 shocks from a defibrillator at the scene and time of the mi (myocardial infarction). I was later told that I had gone a full six minutes with no pulse. On my arrival at hospital I was put into an induced coma and kept on ice, as I like to say, for three days in the intensive critical-care unit. This may sound a little strange, but at this point I feel I had the easiest part to play in this adventure, a silent and yet blissfully unaware starring role.

A series of phone calls and messages went out to my close family and friends on the evening as the news of my mi event, or heart blip as I like to call it, broke and began to circulate. All of my close immediate family were gathered at the intensive care unit within the coronary-care department as soon as possible. They were informed at some stage during that initial period what had happened to me and what the short-term medical plan was to be over the next few hours. My condition was described as critical and they were reassured that everything that could be done was being done. Having said this, my chances of survival were not good and they should prepare for the worst as it was not expected I would survive the night. At this point my youngest daughter Kelly, nineteen at the time, who had been just about to leave for the airport when she received the call, stood tall and threw down the gauntlet in my unconscious absence.

'You don't know my dad then!' she said.

No pressure to stage a comeback then ay! We often laugh about this now. I cannot imagine what they must have gone through: the shock, worry, upset, the roller-coaster of emotions, long days and nights for them all until the relief of the moment I regained consciousness from the coma, I feel guilty for having put them through this.

I had finished my ice cream and was now propped up in bed, feeling much better for having had my hands and face wiped clean. Funny how the simplest of things suddenly began to mean so much. My immediate family were allowed in to see me and I felt like a fraud at this point; I could see they were all so very tired and their eyes red and sore-looking. This, I knew, was down to me and it didn't rest easy with me at all. I don't like to see people, especially my nearest and dearest, down, unhappy and upset. Despite their obvious relief at seeing me awake and talking, I knew the last few days I had put them all through hell; I am so very sorry for this. The really odd thing was I felt absolutely fine, no pain or discomfort, my sore throat and headache had eased up and, apart from feeling tired, I was good to go, or so I thought. We all chatted for a while and generally you could sense the relief, with the mood lightening a fair bit.

I was left alone for a while as my family left to recharge their batteries after the ordeal I had put them through, but I would see them later that evening at visiting time. For now, I lay resting, trying to accept that I had suffered a mi and been clinically dead for six minutes with no pulse and yet here I was, sat up in bed feeling as right as rain. I thought: 'this cannot be right, I'm fine, I will be home tomorrow I reckon'. How wrong can you be? And boy was I ever wrong; I had absolutely no idea what was coming or the impact it would have on my life.

I had a few hours to myself before evening visiting time. I sat up in bed, trying to make sense of what had happened. You see, in my head I couldn't accept that my heart had given out like that, I was pretty fit at the time or so I thought, I was forty-one years young, my weight was good eleven stone, seven pounds for my six-foot frame, I was lean, my diet was clean, the right mix of carbohydrates, proteins, fruits, vegetables, fish, pasta that any cyclist riding an average of 250 miles a week would be consuming. Ok, I will admit to having a sweet tooth and indulge maybe a little more… ok a fair bit more, than I should in the wonderful world of good coffee and cake, but what self-respecting cyclist doesn't I ask you? For the non-cyclists amongst you let me tell you that coffee and cake, café-stops on training rides, or any ride to be frank, are as much a part of cycling as the bike itself. No ride would be complete or worth a mention without a café-stop to consume a delightfully sweet homemade piece of cake or pastry, a cup of tea or, in my case, freshly brewed strong coffee, whether it be a nice English tea room out in the sticks or a good old greasy spoon in the town, or if you're lucky enough, a café in the deep south of France where the pastries and coffee are to die for. It's the law coffee and cake it has to be done! I sat there and just couldn't understand it; I had none of the obvious risk factors, but the fact remained that I had suffered a major mi and there I was, like it or not. None of this made any sense to me. Why had this happened? I could find no answers, only confusion and disbelief at the situation I found myself in.

In my few hours of solace, by comparison to the visiting frenzy that was to follow, I observed the nurses, doctors and consultants going about their business of caring for the many people in their charge like myself. I would do this a lot over the coming weeks. I will say I have the upmost respect and gratitude for these wonderful men and women who are all too often, in my opinion, sadly taken for granted and are under-appreciated, working long unsociable hours, under extreme pressure a lot of that time, very often without breaks. I had numerous conversations with the nurses, who would bring food with them to eat on their well-earned meal breaks but would end up taking it home when their shift was over, the reason being they simply didn't get the chance to take a break. They do such an amazing job and all with a smile on their faces; I for one would not be here today to tell this story without these angels in our midst. I could never thank them enough.

Visiting time arrived that evening. My immediate family came and sat around the bed, they looked a lot better than before and this I found to be a real comfort. In turn they said I was looking far better and had returned to a light shade of pink. Apparently, I would learn later, I had had the complexion and colour similar to that of a corpse for the first few days of my stay in the icu (intensive care unit), we laughed as my daughter said how much I had resembled the family dog whilst I lay in my coma, tongue hanging out, snoring like a pig, all good if you're a Staffordshire bullterrier, not quite so flattering for me I feel. If snoring and sleeping were an Olympic sport, our dog would take gold.

'John you have rather a lot of visitors, I've told them to wait outside, I will let them come in a few at a time if you're feeling up to it?' I looked up at the nurse who conveyed this news with a somewhat concerned look on her face. 'Your family can stay too, that's ok,' she said.

'Yes, that's fine I feel ok,' I replied, thinking 'how many can there be?'

What followed over the next five days was truly the most humbling experience. I was in truth simply overwhelmed by the constant flow and amount of friends from the fire service who came to see me and wish me well, and of course to rip the mick out of me relentlessly. To set the record straight, taking the mick is not offensive, its simply what we do, the time to be concerned is if we are not ripping the mick out of each other. They came by the truck-load, crew after crew, day after day.

I was never alone, the poor nurses gave up in the end as the two people per bed rule simply didn't apply to us. There were ten, fifteen, who knows how many at times, even my consultant joked with me saying, it's like a car park for Dennis out there, friends from outside of brigade came too and the constant presence of my immediate family made the whole adventure very humbling, I truly appreciate all the support and well wishes from all of them, I consider myself very fortunate and thank them all sincerely.

Visiting time came to an end and, at the much-appreciated discretion of the ward sister, my immediate family were allowed a little while longer. My eldest daughter Steph, six months pregnant at the time, was glowing with rosy red cheeks as I recall and this made me feel a whole lot better as I had been worried the stresses of the last few days would have done her absolutely no good at all. She looked well and I was feeling well and happy too. Not long after my cardiology consultant came by and informed me that the following afternoon, we would do some tests and, results dependent, take things from there. How was I feeling? In truth perfectly fine, I said. In my mind I was thinking, get tests done, maybe a tablet or two and I will be home, job done. Wrong again - I really didn't have a clue and my brain simply would not accept the reality of the situation. I remember feeling quite tired but at the same time at peace with myself and happy that I was ok. As the nurse dimmed the lights on the ward I drifted off into a good sound, deep, restful sleep.

I remember the feeling so vividly as this was the last time, I have slept a good unbroken night's sleep to this day. I woke the next morning at 6.30am feeling refreshed and good to go, showered and, with clean pjs on, I made my bed, packed all my gear from the bedside locker into my bag and sat up in the chair next to my neatly made bed thinking, 'right I'm all set, get the tests done, pop some pills and I will be out of here'.

I picked up my book. I was reading Mark Cavendish boy racer, a good read in my opinion, it reminded me of my now brother-in-law, Paul, who like Cavendish has a killer kick in a sprint and that desire to win and a ferocious competitive nature. Paul and I had met at the track back in 1984, spending a few seasons racing and training together. He is a naturally gifted cyclist. Unusually for someone with such a good sprint, Paul can also climb like a rat up a drainpipe. His power-to-weight ratio is incredible. Such a waisted talent in my opinion; I have had the good fortune to ride with some exceptionally strong cyclists over the years but our Paul without a doubt is the strongest bar none.

I passed the morning with tales of Cavendish in the British cycling academy program on the track and his early success on the road winning sprints what a racer that boy is. Lunch time and my family arrived to visit we sat talking. I crowed I would be home later following tests, looking back, they were humoring me, I was convinced I was ok but then, as I say, I had been oblivious to the reality of the situation they had all lived through the previous few days. I was about to join them in that reality I just didn't know it.

I apologise now for my pure ignorance. At this stage my knowledge of anything to do with the heart, coronary system, coronary heart disease, associated tests, medicines, procedures, treatments, causes, cures, rehabilitation was pretty much a big fat zero. So when I was taken down for my angiogram, I had no idea what it involved or what it might reveal. The room in the radiology / x-ray department was in a semi darkened light and cold as I recall lay on the trolley as I call it.

I was given a local anesthetic followed by a small incision made over the artery in my wrist. A long and very thin catheter was inserted into the artery, this was then guided along the artery to my heart where a dye was injected and a series of images and x-rays were taken, followed by some lengthy discussions between the consultants and staff in the room. The whole procedure was pain free, a slightly odd feeling at times and there was a warm sensation as the dye travelled on its journey round my system, but certainly no pain. It was an amazing experience to be honest, to see your own heart at work is quite something, to me at least it all looked good.

The next words from the consultant's mouth hit me like a Joe Frazier left hook, if I had not been lying down already, I would have gone down. Admittedly there was more to the conversation but this is all I clearly remember from it.

'Ok, John, we're going to have to carry out a triple-bypass operation on your heart as the damage is extensive.'

Boom, stop the clocks, did he really just say that? Had I heard it right? Time stood still for a few moments. I was shell shocked, absolutely stunned; the reality of the situation hit me at last and hit me hard. This was definitely not the outcome I had imagined at all; I could hear my own voice inside my head, 'Christ I'm in trouble here, am I going to die? Will I survive this?' I wanted to get up and walk away but my legs would not have let me even if I had tried; they were numb like lumps of concrete, holding me prisoner on the trolley. Up to this point I had been feeling ok, in that split-second right there I felt ill, as though I was one step away from the death I had managed to evade four days earlier. In one short moment my whole world was turned upside down, for the first time in my life I felt vulnerable, a chink was now apparent in my armor, suddenly things had changed and for me it all became very real.

Mortified by the prospect of having to face what amounted to major heart surgery, my immediate concern was how to tell my family especially my daughters. I knew this would hit them hard too, I did not want to see them upset but there was no way of hiding this, it was inevitable and I knew it. Tough times were ahead, and the uncertainty of the outcome filled my mind, this was taking some accepting but what choice did I have? None, absolutely none, there was no Plan B nor any other options available to me. I could hear my dad's voice in my mind. He used to say to me, 'you can only fight what's in front of you.' I guess in this case he was right.

There were a few tears that evening as my family and I discussed the surgery that was to be faced in the near future. I tried my best to make light of it, but I knew as well as they did the seriousness of the situation. My assurances to them that I would be fine and that I was way too stubborn to let this heart blip beat me, gave them little comfort in truth. It hurt me to see them so upset and worried, especially my girls; dads are not supposed to break we are indestructible, but I was on the ropes here and we all knew it.

The surgery was to be carried out at a different hospital a few miles away. I was due to be transferred on Sunday evening; today was Friday I had a few days to reflect on this adventure. So far, it had been quite a ride. The constant stream of visitors continued which was a welcome distraction, I had made some good friends with my fellow patients and the wonderful staff on the hospital ward. By the time Sunday evening arrived, my mood was relaxed and I had surrendered into a state of acceptance with the situation.

It had been a week almost to the minute since my heart blip when the hospital transfer from Russell's Hall took place. I said my goodbyes to my fellow patients and thanked the nurses and doctors who had worked so hard and taken such good care of me. In truth they had kept me alive to this point. No amount of thanks could ever be enough. I will forever be in debt to these amazing people, god bless you all. The doors closed behind me as I was wheeled out of the hospital and into the waiting ambulance. Stage 1 complete, I was heading for Stage 2 at New Cross Hospital, I had no clue what was waiting for me there, maybe just as well. For now, at least, I felt a sense of achievement, I had survived this far, I was still in the race.

2

Holding on at Rock Bottom

My first few days at New Cross Hospital were quite uneventful by comparison to what would follow. The ward on coronary care was light and airy, there were only three of us and the two old boys I was rooming with were great characters, both good old Black Country boys with a dry sense of humor; we had a scream. The staff were lovely, always pleasant and up for the crack as it were. It was a nice place to be, which may sound a little odd but I felt happy and settled there. My family and friends would come visit, we would sit and chat passing the time, I was even allowed to have a gentle walk around at times: round the ward, up and down the maze of corridors, in fact if it had not been for the heart monitor that was attached to my chest with sticky pads and wires I might have completely forgotten why I was there. This was proven to be the calm before the storm.

Tuesday morning arrived along with the ward sister, who informed me that, all being well, my heart surgery was planned for the following afternoon, my consultant surgeon would be around later that day to see me and explain to me the procedure and timetable of events. I admit this news did set my nerves tingling a bit, it was a reminder, as if I should have needed one, as to why I was there. The feeling of being relaxed started to subside almost immediately, odd that!

My lunch order had been taken; it was chicken pie with vegetables and mashed potatoes. Now I will say this, the moans and groans you hear about hospital food being awful, you can't eat it, and so on, for these people I have a question: 'have you ever been hungry? I mean really hungry, to the point where you begin to fantasize about food, any food doesn't matter what it is, a hunger that consumes your mind and every conscious thought within it, a hunger that ties your stomach into a knot of aching discomfort, a hunger that brings on cravings so strong you would willingly beg, borrow and steel, trade your soul to the devil for just a mouthful of even the most vile and unsavory of food, turn you into something little more than a ravenous dog?' Well I have. This is not because I was deprived at any point in my life of being fortunate enough to have my meals; oh no it is simply this: I cycle, I am a cyclist, this is what long days spent in the saddle mile after mile, uphill and down dale at high intensity will do to you. If you do not eat and drink properly on the bike you will, as we say in cycling, bonk (a sudden and disastrous depletion of the body's energy stores, caused by lack of correct nutritional food supply during endurance training or racing). There is no coming back from it either if you allow it to happen, as I have on a few occasions. 'Amateur' I hear you scream; well maybe but even the pros suffer this now and again. My point is this: I don't complain about food, I eat what I am given and I am grateful for it. You could be hungry, truly starving, some poor souls in this world are, be thankful you are not one of them.

My consultant arrived earlier than expected. I was immediately impressed by the man that stood in front of me. He was, I noticed, very smart and well presented, commanding a certain presence. He spoke softly with what I guessed to be an East European accent. Adding to the whole effect of having one of those voices that you can't help being drawn to, and happily listen to for hours in end.

'Good afternoon, Mr. Evans. How are you? My name is Mr Matuszewski,' he said.

We shook hands. I remember thinking, 'I like this man'. He had time for me and took that time to explain the procedure that he would be required to carry out, in such a way that even someone like me could understand. In my simple words not Mr Matuszewski I stress, I understood the procedure like this: my chest would be cut open, the sternum cut in half length ways, the largest veins would be taken from either my arms or legs, my heart would then be replumbed, bypassing the arteries at the inlet and outlet points - simple right? What! Really! How amazing is it that a person can do such an incredible procedure? How gifted and skillful was this man? How long must he have studied? How hard must he have worked? How much effort to absorb the knowledge and perfect the skills necessary to do this? I felt very humbled and instantly had the upmost respect for this man, what an incredible individual.

The risks involved and the possible outcomes were discussed, along with the basic timetable of events pre- and post-surgery. His calmness and approach to the whole situation put me at ease. I had confidence in him but, make no mistake, despite me telling myself, 'it's going to be ok John you can handle this,' I was scared. I was no stranger to pain or surgery; I had already experienced a lot of both in my lifetime, mainly thanks to cycling. Crashing is part of the sport and if you don't want to crash and break yourself now and again, don't take up cycling simple as that. I got the impression however, and rightly so, this surgery would turn out to be a hell of a lot more than the usual quick, off to sleep, in, pin, plate and screws, out, stitched up, wake up, job done, bone-repair surgery I was used to. This was a whole other level and the odds of survival were not that great, I would find out later just how much they were stacked against me. I still squirm uncomfortably when I think about what I said when I was asked by this great man if I had any questions: 'Can you please leave my legs alone and take the veins from my arms?' My inner chimp had taken over and answered for me, I don't need my arms to be 100% to cycle, a few veins short not a problem, right?

We all have moments we wish we could rewind and erase, I guess, and this was my finest ever. I take this opportunity in black and white to whole heartedly apologise to Mr Matuszewski for saying such a stupid thing. How embarrassing. In truth did it matter where the veins were taken from? Of course not, this man and I were about to embark on an adventure together where he would literally have my life in his hands. My embarrassment soon left me as the realization of how serious the situation was began to dawn. We shook hands again and I thanked him for his time. I was then left alone to contemplate the upcoming events.

Visiting time that afternoon and evening took on an uneasy feel. My family and I discussed the upcoming surgery; I answered their questions and concerns as best I could with my basic and limited knowledge. I tried to make light of the situation as much as possible but there was no getting away from the fact it would be no walk in the park for any of us directly involved. I have always felt, by a long way I had the easiest role to play during the surgery, after all I would be asleep, resuming my role as the blissfully unaware star of the show. My family would be put through the torture, stress and uncertainty during the long hours waiting for news: 'Had I made it through the operation?' 'Was I ok?' 'Had it all gone as planned?' I feel for them; I can't imagine what they went through during that time. Also, Mr Matuszewski, my consultant, and his team, the pressure these amazing people must perform under is immense: long hours, no breaks. They don't have the luxury of making mistakes; it has to be right first time 100% of the time or people die, it's that simple. Can you imagine working in a situation like that? Yes, I know they have the training but let's not take anything away from these amazing people; they work miracles every day. I for one am certainly glad they do.

Visiting time came to a close that evening; the hugs and squeezes of the hands were just that little bit longer and little bit tighter as this would be our last time together until after the surgery. The tears welling up in the eyes of my girls confirmed what we were all thinking but no one was saying: potentially this could be our last moment of time together, full stop. Only the skills of Mr Matuszewski, his dedicated team and the Lord God Almighty himself could determine the outcome of my fate from here on in.

As the sun came up on the day of the surgery, I recall thinking how splendid it was to see the sun in all its warm glowing glory. Inside I smiled to myself, pleased indeed that if this was to be my last dawn it had been a good one.

'Good morning, John.' The nurse arrived to take my blood pressure and pulse as she had done on the hour every hour since my arrival. It was all pretty normal for me bp 110/70 pulse 43, which may sound a touch low but cycling will do that for you. Low pulse rates are very common among cyclists, it was not unusual for me for my resting pulse rate to be in the high thirties. It came to mind that I had once read somewhere the great Spanish five-time Tour de France winner, Miguel Indurain, or the big Mig as we call him, had once recorded a resting pulse of 27bpm, what an amazing athlete and truly great cyclist.

I was allowed a few sips of water in order to take my ever-growing mountain of medication, that was breakfast sorted –

'nil by mouth' for me at least till after the surgery which was due at 13:30 hours.

The nurse smiled. 'How are you feeling, John? It's a big day for you.'

'Still ticking, which is the main thing,' I replied.

We laughed a little. Looking back, I think we were both nervous for me, but it was a nice moment, one of many, the staff were always so warm and caring, very nice people.

The morning passed slowly, my nerves beginning to build. The anesthetist came to see me; she was softly spoken and took the time to explain what would happen a little later that day; we worked through and filled in all the required paperwork and I signed my consent.

'That's it no going back now. I'm all yours.'

'You seem to be handling the situation very well, John. This is good,' she said smiling.

'Yes I feel fine,' I replied however I owe this young lady an apology: I was lying. I was dying a thousand deaths inside, feeling sick with apprehension for the upcoming surgery. For the first time I could feel the pressure bearing down on me; I was afraid and feeling very alone. My inner chimp was rattling his cage. Don't get me wrong, he was up for the fight which lay ahead but he was not happy at all.

The ward sister and hospital porter arrived. It was show time. I was all ready to be taken to theatre; I had changed earlier into my gown, my costume if you like for my starring role to be played out in the operating theatre along with the cast of dedicated surgeons, anesthetists, nurses and so forth. It was, I am sure, a performance of life-saving brilliance, such was the expertise and talent of the cast.

The air temperature took a noticeable drop as I was wheeled through the double doors into the anesthetists room which had that wonderful sterile, bleachy smell about it. I was impressed and filled with confidence by the cleanliness of the place, everything in order and laid out immaculately. For a few short moments I felt calm and almost at peace with the situation. The doors behind me opened and Mr Matuszewski along with the anesthetist appeared at the bedside, they were suited and booted in surgical robes head-to-toe, just their eyes showing between the masks and caps. I recall thinking how smart they both looked. The anesthetist began her preparations while Mr Matuszewski and I had a chat.

I am enormously impressed that this man always has time for me. Softly spoken and genuine, he discussed various things but for me the most poignant moment came with these words:

'Mr Evans (a short silent pause) - John - I will do my very best for you.' He was looking me straight in the eye.

I smiled. 'I know you will and that's all I can ask, I trust you, thank you.'

I could sense he smiled under the mask; he then made his way through the double doors in front of me which led directly into theatre. Boom! my mind went into overdrive, Christ there was a chance I wouldn't actually make this: it hit me like a freight train, he knew it I knew it. This could be it I was thinking.

Calmly the anesthetist said, 'I have to leave you for a few moments then it will be time, John.'

Now I am not a religious man in the sense that I go to church every Sunday because I don't, but I do go along now and again when I feel the need to. Usually I attend at Christmas time and Easter. However, I often have a chat in my own mind with the big man upstairs, this was one of those moments as I lay there alone. I was not looking to make my peace with God or ask forgiveness for my sins, no, I was pure and simple asking for help. I was going to give everything I had to give, empty the tank as we say in cycling, but I wasn't sure that was enough to get me through. Was I enough as a man, was I strong enough, literally did I have the heart? In truth, I doubted my ability to stand up to what was coming, so there, alone on the trolley, I asked God for a little help. I asked for help to find the strength I needed to pull me through; I asked for him to watch over my family and friends and take care of them through their lives if indeed it was my time to leave them. I was consumed by the idea that I was now staring death in the face. It was not good; in my mind I said my goodbyes to my family, my children, my grandchildren. I was convinced this was my curtain-call and I was on the last lap, going full gas, the checkered flag was out but there would be no victory lap this time, just the end.

The anesthetist returned This eased my downward spiral of emotions, as she set about the business of attaching equipment to me that would be needed during the surgery. Then came the time to insert the canular into my vein, she was very careful with everything she did, talking to me the whole time, it was very reassuring and, boy, did I need some reassuring! At last we were good to go. All that remained was to administer the anesthetic itself which would send me off for potentially the eternal sleep. Above the double doors leading directly into theatre the clock read 13:28, I recall thinking 'perfectly on time'. My anesthetist was of a Mediterranean origin and had the most wonderful accent to her voice. What I noticed most of all about her, probably due to the fact this was the only visible part of her, other than the surgery scrubs she wore, was her eyes - she had the darkest, deepest eyes I have ever seen; you could have drowned in the depth of her eyes.

As she administered the anesthetic into my vein, she spoke softly and gently squeezed my hand. I glanced briefly at the clock: bang on time, 13:30, focusing back to the gaze of my anesthetist. I looked deep into her eyes as the drugs began to work their magic and take me off into no man's land. If I was never to wake then I wanted the last vision I had to be the kind caring eyes of another human being, everything became a blur and I was gone.

There was music coming from somewhere.

'Staring at the bottom of your glass, hoping one day you will make a dream last, but dreams come slow and they go so fast.'

Maybe it was just in my head. To this day I am not sure but those were the first words and sounds that came to my ears after nine-and-a-half hours of open-heart surgery, the song has stuck with me and the words are forever engrained on my mind. I have lost count of the times I have listened to this song since that day; I have it on repeat on my playlist, it's my go-to song when I need a helping hand, a little extra motivation, a little extra push up a long climb, or just those times when I need to sit down and shut the world outside for a while. It's always there in my mind; it picks me up, motivates me, reminds me no matter how bad I am feeling inside, I can draw breath, gather myself together and go again. I am not saying it's easy or the kind of thing works for everyone, but I have always got lost in music and this song helps me. I am a great believer in whatever works for you just do it; we are all individuals at the end of the day, and all need a push now and then.

It's said there is an equal and exact opposite to everything. The music in my head faded away, replaced by the horrendous noises of machines, monitors, drips, and God only knows what else. I still find these noises and anything similar offensive and to some level distressing today. I was hooked up to so much equipment, surrounded by noise; I couldn't move; worst of all I couldn't see; for the second time in as many weeks I was blind. The fear took over me again.

It was deja vue, a soft voice next to me. 'Lay still, John.'

Again I was gagging on a tube being gently and carefully removed from my throat, I was regaining consciousness.

'Lay still, John. You're in icu recovery, you're doing well.' There was a reassuring squeeze of the hand.

'I can't see,' I kept repeating to myself almost in a panic.

'Your vision will return. It may be a little blurred for a while, but it will come back.'

As always, I put all my faith and trust in these amazing people who cared for me. As always, I was right to do so. Slowly the darkness turned to blurred light and shadows moving around, eventually give way to a misty view of my surroundings. The scene was similar to the cockpit of an aircraft: a sea of lights, red, green, orange, white, blue, some flashing, some moving, every direction I looked, and the noise, oh boy, the noise of those monitors and machines went straight through me. It was pure psychological torture non-stop; it was awful, necessary, I fully appreciated that - but awful in the extreme.

I fully understand that, as individuals, we all have our limits, including our toleration of pain, now I am not saying mine are any greater or less than anyone else, I just know mine that's all. I was no stranger to pain, throughout the course of my forty-one years thus far, I had broken just about everything there is to break: wrists, ankles, arms, ribs, hands. You name it, I have probably broken it. I am full of pins, plates, screws, I have more scars than a pin cushion thanks to many surgeries along the way, mostly down to my own stupidity and a lifetime spent racing and pedaling bikes, such is the nature of cycling, plus my seeming God-given talent for being able to pedal a bike far quicker than my bike-handling skills safely allow, but, hey, we can't have it all, right?

This was a new kind of pain however, it was pure, cleansing and intense, on the classic give-me-a-number-between-one-and-ten scale, this baby was off the scale, infinity and beyond. Whatever my limit and threshold for tolerating pain, believe me, I was on it. I couldn't have taken any more. This was a proven fact right there and then. A team of nurses arrived at my bedside, I cannot recall exactly why but something had to be done that involved me being rolled onto my side for a few seconds then returned to flat on my back,

As I am now, that would have been simple enough, but then factor in I had wires, tubes, iv lines sticking in and out of me everywhere, arms, neck, chest, all the orifices you don't want things in and some I didn't realize existed - I literally could not move there were so many. I was a fly caught in a spider's web of medical brilliance, kept captive within its life-saving maze.

'Cross your arms over your chest, John.'

A rolled blanket, I think it was, was placed gently across my chest which was now held together with metal coils having been cut and split down the middle during the surgery.

'Hold my hand, John, and take a deep breath. Hold it in while we turn you. Don't breath out; it will only be for a few seconds.'

I did as I was told. The proof I was at my limits, as if I needed it, came within the next ten seconds or so that followed. I breathed in; it was pure agony to inhale a full breath at this point. The nurse squeezed my hand as I was carefully turned on my side by the staff who surrounded me, instantly sweat formed on my forehead and began to run down my face. I do not have the words to describe the pain as I was moved; my vision faded in to a black and white snow storm, as though watching the old tv we had in our house as kids. Hanging on by a thread, the nurse telling me to hold on and squeeze her hand, her voice began to fade away, I was drifting somewhere between this world and unconsciousness; I sensed my grip loosening, the breath slowly seeping out through my clenched teeth. In cycling terminology I was pedaling in the red zone, being dropped by the bunch, the elastic was beginning to break, I was beat, I couldn't hold on any longer it was too much.

Her voice filtered back through the wall of pain: 'Well done, John. It's all done now.'

I recall thinking 'thank you.' I was in a pain-induced stupor and - I don't say this lightly given the brilliance and hard work of Mr Matuszewski who in my opinion had just performed a miracle and saved my life - if you had placed a loaded gun at my head at this point in time I would gladly have pulled the trigger simply to escape the pain. Looking back, this was a defining moment for me in how I look at and think about things today, a life lesson learned, if you like, the hard way. It's amazing how my perspectives and priorities were changed in that instant.

The nurses who cared for me were brilliant and did everything they could to make me comfortable. I guess it was around midnight when the light over my strangely moving bed was dimmed, this was such a relief to my eyes and thumping headache. I recall willing every drop of the morphine in the drip next to me to fall, to run into me like a river to numb the pain but of course it was measured and correct as was every minute detail of my surgery and aftercare, the knowledge and skill of these people is a sight to behold - pure brilliance.

I rested that night but didn't sleep, not so much because of the pain, which after a few hours of constant drip-fed morphine was becoming more tolerable as long as I didn't move too much, more because of the relentless beeping and pipping sounds coming from all the equipment I was hooked up to. Of all the process from start to finish, this was what bothered and affected me the most, these noises really got inside my head, there was no escape from them. To this day similar noises drive me insane, I can't bear to hear them, psychologically they send me straight back to the icu, trapped in my web in my darkest hours.

The next morning, I was feeling a lot better, maybe twenty percent of my normal self but I was convinced the night before I was one step away from my end, so twenty percent I was happy to take. Despite the severe pain in my chest where I had been chopped open like a spatchcock chicken I felt reasonably ok, a bit shallow drawing breath as it hurt like hell to take in a lung-full for sure, but I figured, 'I'm breathing, I can see, hang in there, John, you can do this.'

Suddenly and I had no clue as to how or why I hadn't noticed this before, I realized every time I moved my left leg it hurt, not real bad pain, just uncomfortable and sore, you know, like a good old snake bite we would inflict on each other as kids; yes, we were a strange bunch I know. I couldn't see as my legs were covered with a sheet; I couldn't figure it out and was about to try and attract the attention of the very busy, but always hugely attentive, nurses to ask why. I found myself looking at my arms, boom! There was the terrifying answer plain as day.

Apart from a few canular iv lines going in to supply me with the happy juice, (morphine) and other drugs my slowly recovering body craved so much, they were perfect, no bandages, no signs of anything unusual, I didn't need to ask or look, I knew now the discomfort and soreness I was experiencing in my left leg, was from the incision that ran from just above the ankle up to my inner thigh just below the groin, the large vein that runs the length of my left leg had been removed during the surgery, to use for bypassing the arteries of my heart. I was mortified, devastated. Would my leg be stiff? Would it function properly? Would I be able to pedal properly and push as I had before? I was distraught. Physically it was the least of my worries, psychologically for me this was immense.

The whole situation was now catching up with me, my psychological threshold for coping was now also at its limit, I was being completely overwhelmed and this was never more apparent than later that same afternoon. With help from my nurse I had managed to get from the bed into a special orthopedic armchair of sorts; it was a move of little more than a few feet but had taken every ounce of strength and will power I had left, it was agony, but we made it.

The nurse smiled. 'Your daughters have come to see you, John.'

My spirits were lifted all be it temporarily at the news. From my, now seated, position I could see out of the icu unit and away down the long corridor that led to it. I tried to tidy myself up as much as you can in a hospital gown with a million wires and tubes sticking out of you. My daughters are both tough cookies; I would learn later that my eldest, Steph hadn't made it past the waiting room before feeling ill, but Kelly pushed on regardless of the fact that she hates needles and blood in general. She came into view at the end of the corridor, walking towards me. She smiled and waved; I lifted my hand in response, and then it happened, the colour drained from her face. As she drew closer, the smile disappeared, her step slowing; I knew what was about to happen I had seen it before. Bang! Down she went in a heap on the floor, out cold, the sight of me with me fine array of tubes, wires, drips and monitors was too much; she passed out before she made it to the doors. The nurses quickly went to her aid.

Although I knew she would be perfectly ok, this was the final blow that broke me, psychologically. I cracked, there was my little girl out cold on the floor and there was nothing I could do, not a dam thing; I could hardly move and certainly not get up. She was barely thirty feet away and I couldn't help her, I was completely useless to her and I just had to sit there and watch. It broke my spirit, it broke my heart, I am so very sorry. Of course, she was fine she came around but walked away down the corridor. She told me later that she just couldn't bear to see me in the state I was in and I can understand that. This was my lowest point, physically and psychologically I was beat; I had taken all I could and I had nothing more to give. A lump in my throat and tears welling up in my eyes, I was falling apart, don't you dare!! My inner chimp was screaming at me to hold it together, I clenched my teeth and fists hard, trying to refocus and hold on, the chimp screaming to fight on.

Sometimes things happen for a reason, I believe this anyway.

'John, are you ok?' asked the nurse at just that moment. I looked up; as always, she was smiling. She could see I was down and struggling. 'John, in the morning if you feel up to it and want to give it a try, if you can walk a lap of the icu, you will be allowed back up to the general ward.'

I felt myself grinning. 'That's good news, thank you. I'll be ready.'

She laughed out loud. 'John I believe you will.'

My inner chimp was going bananas, he was happily swinging in his tree. He knew, I knew, that this was all we needed; I was about to turn the corner. It wasn't going to be easy, but in a small way this was the start of my journey, to where I didn't yet know but it felt like the beginning. I was not back, nowhere near; I had hit rock bottom and hit it hard but, I don't know how, I had managed to hold on, dig in, suffer and endure. It was time to look up and go again.

3

The gift of life, Gruffalo & coconut.

As was the case with any race I had ridden or any challenge, usually cycling-orientated, I had taken on in my life, pre-event stomachache and bundles of wound-up nervous energy were built up inside me. I was sat up ready and waiting to embark on my maiden voyage around the icu ward. It could have been maybe thirty metres at the most all the way round, but in my present condition I knew this was a long way and I was uncertain how my body would stand up to the challenge that lay before me. All I knew for sure was that this was my shot at freedom, my bid to escape the icu and, in my head, all the noises and equipment holding me captive. The nurse arrived with a smile as always, by her side a rather portly and very jolly looking chap, with a broad grin and a tuft of ginger hair sprouting in all directions. This was the man along with the ward sister I had to impress and prove my worthiness to be set free.

I stood up slowly, along with the heart monitors and iv drips; I took a few steps forward to mount, or at least hold, my sweet ride for this epic one-lap race. My beloved trek road bike had been replaced by a Zimmer frame but it had wheels, so it was good enough for me.

'Come on, little Joe!' (That's my inner chimp. Yes, I know, he has a name.) 'We can do this.'

Off we went, the cardiology physio pulling the trolley, the nurse by my side, me on the Zimmer. It was hard going; my leg was on fire and every step felt like a hot poker was being pressed against it. My lungs were screaming at me. I still couldn't draw a full breath without being in agony so I was sipping air as economically as I could. That's one thing competitive cycling teaches you: how to breath efficiently and be as economical with your efforts as possible depending on the intensity and how much oxygen your body demands as recompense for whatever you're pushing it through. My heart was pounding, thumping on the inside of my chest like a hammer, the monitor rolling behind me was working overtime. It was pretty much full on by this point, but I was moving, I was on it, the sweat running down my face, blowing like a train, ten metres, fifteen metres and counting. I was burning up.

'If you need a break, John, it's ok. We can stop a while.

What? Really! I pushed on round the nurse's station at the top of the ward, I was on the home straight now and my breathing steadied. I started to adjust, getting my second wind if you like. Launching my sprint for the line, full gas now, just a few more metres, I could smell victory. I had made the lap; there was no medal to hang around my neck but I had won my freedom. This was the most precious prize of all; I had won my ticket out of the icu, I would be back on the general ward by the afternoon. The psychological boost I gained from this small victory was massive.

The cardiology physio reappeared a short time after lunch armed with a wheelchair of sorts and along with him the hospital porter. It was time to say my goodbyes and thanks to the amazing nurses and staff on the icu coronary care unit, without whom I would certainly not be here today. I will be forever in their debt no question about it. When I was down, really down, in my darkest hours, they were there, angels every one of them, thank you. I had one request, and at the discretion of the staff nurse I was allowed to walk from my bed to the doors which led out onto the corridor. I had been wheeled into this place unconscious following the heart surgery, a little closer to death perhaps than was comfortable shall we say, but regardless of the state I was in I was damn sure I was walking out of there on my own two feet. Slowly I walked to the doors and out to the next phase of my journey. Insignificant as this may sound, to me it was immense; it was something I simply had to do and needed to do. My stubborn nature was waking inside me once more.

Visiting time back up on the general cardiology ward was quite an emotional affair. It was the first time I had seen my immediate family properly since the surgery. There were lots of smiles and a good few tears. Despite how rough I looked, there was still a lot of relief that I was alive and ticking, doing reasonably well considering. I opened cards full of best wishes; it was generally a nice atmosphere and I was happy and comforted by the smiles and the clear relief on all the faces in front of me; it was a lovely moment. Evening visiting followed much the same pattern, when it was time to say, 'good night, see you tomorrow,' with a degree of ease and confidence for the first time in a long while. It was fair to say I was feeling relaxed and, although still in a fair amount of pain, quite at peace with things generally.

I sat up with a pillow behind me in the chair next to the bed, I was more comfortable sat up; my chest just hurt too much to lay down, I couldn't bear it. It would be months before I could lay down and even now I cannot lay on my side - but I figure it's an easy price to pay. Looking out of the window I could see the sun lower itself behind the grassy tree-line beyond the grounds of the park which lay adjacent to the hospital. There was a light breeze gently fanning me through the slightly opened window; the lukewarm feel and smell of the air made me smile; I was getting sleepy and, as I drifted off, I was thinking of long summer evening rides out through country lanes between fields of golden crops and the woods where the air is pure and your lungs can gorge themselves as you power along, pushing the big gears, taking in the amazing scenery that is our wonderful countryside, such are the joys of cycling in the summertime. Cycling is very much a pleasure-and-pain scenario; I drew this comparison now with a wry smile. I had certainly earned this pleasure following an equally pure amount of pain. I was now on the up, this had been a good day.

The sun came up on that Saturday morning. I had slept better on and off and sat up in the chair, which I had decided this was my best option for comfort, and the nurses didn't mind. I was happy; they were happy.

As the sun found its way along the grass and footpath outside, it eventually reached our window to fill the room with that bone-warming natural light and warmth only a sunny morning can give you. I felt good. I had this odd feeling about the day as if something had changed but in a good way; I couldn't explain it, maybe it was an omen or a sign, I don't know, but the feeling was there.

The consultant, Mr Matuszewski, would be along to see me shortly. I had just enjoyed my first cup of tea since the surgery without the foul metallic taste of potassium as an accompaniment- you simply cannot beat a nice cup of tea first thing. Right on cue Mr Matuszewski arrived, it was a surreal moment: my two roommates were still sleeping while Mr Matuszewski and I sat talking, looking out at the blue sky and sunshine. It was all so very matter of fact, we discussed the surgery, it would appear things had been worse than expected. I was initially meant to have triple-heart-bypass surgery but, as it turned out, once the surgery was underway it became clear that my heart and arteries were in a worse state than first thought. It was explained to me that in fact six bypass grafts had to be done. Apparently, this is quite rare. The surgery had taken nine and a half hours of this incredible man's life to save mine, no question about it. There was a significant amount of damage and scarring on my heart, which apparently, as a muscle, was quite large. I like to think that in some way a lifetime spent cycling and exercising my heart, while, yes I admit, pushing it to the limit, also contributed to its ability to withstand the trauma it had gone through. My heart had taken a beating, yes indeed, but had stood up to it. I was quite proud of my ticker.

It was explained to me that everything possible, that could be done for my heart had been done. It had taken a lot of surgery, but I had responded well. I would need to take the recovery and aftercare seriously and give the time necessary in order to recover. I was in complete awe of this man; I asked how long I could expect the repairs (my terminology) to last, as I got the feeling the surgery was a one-shot deal somehow.

So, if I eat clean, live clean, rest properly and, well, take damn good care of my heart, rough estimate ten good years, anything after that is a bonus, since recurring problems may or may not arise. Medical advances move forward fairly quickly, so who knows what may be available in the future should the need arise? For now, this man had worked nothing short of a miracle; I was alive and ticking, a few more good scars of which I am proud. What is it they say about a scar? It is a reminder that you were stronger than whatever tried to hurt you, hmm maybe, you be the judge. I am fortunate that I don't mind my scars however; I know this is not the case for everyone and I truly feel for these people.

Then came the million-dollar question, as far as I was concerned anyway: how long before I could get back to my cycling? I was concerned, you see, about losing the fitness I had built up over the last winter and spring. I had been pedaling well, my legs were in good shape, my average week was a good 250 miles training and the usual 80-miles-a-week steady commute on top, I didn't want to see it all go, I was keen to get back in the saddle.

'Realistically consider that you may not return to cycling.'

For a moment my world stopped turning, the chain and sprockets ground to a sudden and instant halt. The bottom fell out of my soul right there right then. From my first hand painted bike, (big sister's hand-me-down but I didn't care) to racing round the park on my boxer then grifter with my mates as a kid, to racing for my club and country on the track, to the thousands of miles on the road and off it, the end-to-end John o' Groats to Land's End ride, to training all weathers and all seasons, even battling on for miles against the snow with my friend pike, thousands up on thousands of hours riding trapped between the pleasure and pain where a cyclist spends much of his or her existence - this was all gone, wiped out in an instant. I was absolutely gutted and, excuse the pun, heartbroken.

The feeling lasted, I would estimate, somewhere between one and maybe three seconds at best. To explain, there are two things I am bound to be eternally grateful for, and forever in debt to Mr Matuszewski: one, the miracle that was the six-graft bypass surgery that saved me and gave me my life back; two, the motivation I needed to pick myself up, shake the dust off and go again. In an instant he gave me that. Boom! It hit me like a freight train, the desire and unquenchable yearning to get out of the hospital as soon as possible and get back on the bike. Those who know me best will tell you how stubborn I can be. You wanna light my fire: just tell me, 'I can't', 'you won't', or 'you got to', and so on; the second I hear this it's over, you lost already or I died trying. It's that simple. I had already decided in my head that on 9th June 2014 exactly one year to the day since my heart mi and clinically dead for six minutes blip, I would be riding my bike on some adventure somewhere, not to prove anyone wrong but to prove to myself and maybe a few others, that you can achieve anything you want to in this life; you just got to want it bad enough, and believe you can. This great man had bestowed on me the two greatest gift:, he had not only saved my life and given it back to me but, without realizing it, he had given me the self-belief that I needed too.

Our conversation continued for a while. It was put to me that I might be able to return home as early as the Wednesday, four days from then. I was responding well to the surgery and my stats were improving quickly, however there would be a test of sorts that I would have to pass. A protected stairwell lay at the end of the general ward: I would have to walk unaided up one flight of the stairs, which were roughly twice as long, as your standard domestic staircase at home, without stopping and/or my pulse rising more than might normally be expected for someone in my present condition. Easy right? Well, we would see. I had four days to train for it and put in some hard miles between visiting and medical stuff. Mr Matuszewski and I shook hands and I thanked him. What can you say to a man who saved your life and gave it back to you?

I spent the next four days training, which basically meant I would walk, wheeling my trolley full of monitors and the iv drips I was still hooked up to, out of the room, down the corridor and back and repeat this as many times as I could before fatigue set in or my heart rate set off the alarm on the monitor, in which case I was made to stop and return to my chair. My nurses were very understanding. In all honesty, I think I drove them mad, but they could see how much I needed to do this and were sympathetic to my efforts. My training continued every spare moment my body and nurses would allow me to. I was on it.

I have read so many books in my lifetime written by and for the greats of cycling, the giants of the road, the likes of Fausto Coppi, Jacques Anquetil, Bernard Hinault, Stephan Roche, Sean Kelly, Lemond, Indurain, Cadel Evans, Lance Armstrong, George Hinchapie, the great Eddie Merckx, and of course my idol Laurent Fignon, to name but a few. What all these men have in common apart from being the greatest cyclists to grace our sport is their ability to suffer and endure. I mean suffer in agony day after day when every muscle and sinew in their body, mind and soul is screaming at them to stop, somehow, they push on through the pain. This is why they are who they are and achieve what they do, and, yes, inspire people like me and many others to push on. I drew inspiration from their stories and lives many times over the years, but never more than now and over the coming months.

Some of you will undoubtedly be thinking, yeh right they do it with drugs, especially given some of the names I have mentioned drawing inspiration from. We all have opinions and we are fortunate to have that right, so as best I can, in brief, I will give you mine. Cycling in any form at any level is hard, pure and simple, if you can't learn to love the pain and suffering then don't go cycling. Is there such a thing as a clean cyclist? I would love to believe there is, but I have my doubts. Define doping? - well my interpretation is this: from elite pros doing epo at the highest level, to a nobody like me popping pain killers and caffeine to numb the pain before getting on the bike every ride, what's the difference? Did you ever take an energy gel or drink? Take vitamin supplements? Use an inhaler perhaps? Medication that may or may not boost performance. And what about protein shakes or stopping at a café for coffee and cake

(=caffeine and sugar) as I have many times, Boom! We all dope with no exceptions on some level or another, that's just cycling. My point is this, whatever your opinion, these men are as hard as coffin nails with or without, hard men who live a lifetime of suffering to win bike races. I respect their drive, focus, hard work and determination. They light it up for millions of fans and the media around the world year after year. The bikes don't pedal themselves; it is not easy. Give the hardships of the sport some respect, enjoy our sport, enjoy cycling, take it for what it is. For the judges and haters out there, do something else is my advice. You don't win the tour eating cheese sandwiches.

My training continued over the next few days and I was feeling quite happy that I was able to do a little more each day. The good spirits and banter continued in our corner of the ward. Generally I was enjoying my time and starting to feel a whole lot better. My constant stream of visitors continued to brighten my days and I was given various gifts from time to time, two of which stood out: my lucky mascot - a small fist-sized Gruffalo, which cheered me up no end, and, bizarre as this may sound, a coconut, bought along by my good friend Big George, nicknamed so after the great George Hinchapie for being such a beast on the bike.

In he came, big grin on his face.

'How you doing mate? I've bought you this, a coconut.' I mean, why wouldn't you? We roared. It was one of those ridiculously funny moments; you had to be there I guess, but it was a great pick-me-up. I still have both the Gruffalo and the coconut to this day. Big George and I had spent countless hours and miles cycling together over the years, both on road and off it. He is himself an exceptionally strong cyclist; he has this ability to sit there and power along pushing monster big gears relentlessly, a natural powerhouse, strong, durable. It came as no shock to me when I told him of my plan to do a ride of some kind on the first anniversary of my heart blip, that he cut in straight away saying, 'mate wherever and whatever you decide to ride you can put my name down first on the team sheet, I will ride with you.' The only shock was that Big George had been off the bike himself for almost three years, due to two separate hip replacement surgery's and, by his own admission, a serious lack of motivation and self-belief as a result. I didn't need to ask if he was sure; I knew it was a done deal. I have met few people in my life more stubborn than me and Big George is one of them. The idea was born, the seed was planted and watered in both of us. We didn't know where or what the target for our adventure would be yet, but it was on. We had a good year to train, suffer and drag each other along to get there. Would we make it? The odds were stacked heavily against us at this point. Hell, if it was easy where would be the fun in that?

This was going to be as much of a battle for Big George as it was for me. The whole crazy idea was gathering momentum. Big George is no quitter; I knew, no matter how hard this comeback would be for us, he would push me when I needed it - and I would return the favor. My moral and general psychological mood was improving: something was happening, a good feeling, exciting. I had something to aim for, focus on, with Big George along for the ride I had gained confidence too. However first I had to keep clocking laps of the corridor; there was a flight of stairs to be climbed and they had my name on them.

As evening descended, I was feeling confident, motivated, ready for tomorrow's stair test and ultimately my crack at freedom, my ticket out of the hospital. I discussed with my family the prospect of being allowed home the next day. The mood was light and optimistic now, this whole adventure so far had taken its toll on everyone around me, they had all suffered so much, probably more so than me. I was directly involved as were they, but they had endured the long hours of waiting, wondering, hoping that I had enjoyed the luxury of sleeping through, I hoped that tomorrow would bring relief.

The morning came for my much anticipated, by me at least, attack on the stairwell, my bid for freedom. Like a cat on hot bricks, I waited for the nurse and physio who would accompany me. I was eager to get on with it; I had put in the hard miles up and down the corridors, I was ready, the moment had arrived at last. Walking steadily down to the end of the corridor, as if on a warm-up lap, just turning the legs, getting loose, not burning any energy that would be needed in the effort to come. We arrived in the stairwell, which was typical of this kind of place: bare featureless walls, metal handrails and edging strips on the concrete steps, cold, silent, barren, uninviting in the extreme. It was perfect for me I could hate the place with a passion.

For the first time in just over two weeks I was unplugged from everything. It was an amazing feeling to be set free from the medical chains that had bound me and had been dragging around with me for what had seemed like an eternity. It was explained to me what I had to do and that I should take my time, only to hold the rail if I needed to stop etc. No disrespect intended, but I simply wasn't listening at all. I was focused completely on the top step, my gaze fixed, foot ready on the first step as though lined up on the starting grid of the track. You are under starter's orders, silence falls waiting for the starter to pull the tape, before the noise of the crowd hits you like freight train and every muscle and sinew of your body explodes as you heave the first pedal down hard to get everything moving, your heart ready to burst under the strain. It's such a rush and a great feeling. Admittedly this was not so dramatic, but to me in that moment it was.

Like him or loathe him, Lance Armstrong is a lot of things to a lot of people but to me he is an inspiration. Forget the cycling, that isn't what I'm talking about here. If you have read his early books, as I have on numerous occasions, you will understand where I am coming from. First off, I must stress that I don't consider my heart blip anywhere near the battle that cancer patients face; my condition amounts to no more than a flesh wound by comparison in my opinion. My heart goes out to all those battling this cruel disease. No, what I am referring to here is the sheer determination and will to survive that drove Armstrong on, his stubborn, keep-getting-up, keep-moving-forward attitude; the man just would not quit, that's what inspires me about him. As I waited on the stairs, I recalled a couple of things he had written about during his time in hospital battling cancer. He would walk dragging his iv drips along the covered walkway linking two sections of the hospital, when he should really have used a wheelchair; he would drink double the amount of water required of him, despite the awful sickness he was suffering as a result of the chemical cocktail that is chemotherapy, the putrid metallic taste in his mouth making each mouthful a battle in itself. He did this not because of his superstar cyclist status but because he was a man deep down in his darkest hour, digging in, suffering, enduring, being stubborn, fighting back the best way he could. That's what inspired me.

This was my covered walkway, my glasses of water right here and now. As I set off on my long journey up the stairs, I was determined not to stop or show the pain - and believe me there was plenty of that; I was in bits. I kept going one step after another, I made it to the top – freedom! I don't know why I did this, it just kind of happened, but I carried on across the landing area and began to climb the second flight of stairs, pumped up in the zone, burning up, sweat pouring out of me, heart trying to burst out of my rib cage but I didn't care, my inner chimp was having his moment, he was on it. I stood or, more in truth, leaned on the rail at the top of the second flight of stairs completely shot, exhausted and in bits, but boy did it feel good to push hard again.

I received a good telling-off from my nurse and justifiably so, but it was another step forward for me and one I am glad I took when I look back now. On my return to the ward I received the good news I would be allowed home that afternoon. Following some paperwork to sign - instructions on the mountain of drugs I would need to take daily for the rest of my life - three small wires were gently removed from my chest and some stiches. I was now free from it all. The scars were all that remained and they were beauties.

I said my goodbyes to my room mates and the wonderful staff who had taken such amazing care of me and, I may add, put up with my crazy training regime. You're angels every single one of you, no thanks could ever be enough.

Two and a half weeks earlier I had been rushed into hospital, unconscious with little chance of survival, on a trolley with machines keeping me alive and now, the double-doors opened and the warmth of the sun hit my face. Smiling I walked out of there on my own two feet; I was free, I was going home.

4

Setting the Target: Sunshine and Sea.

It took a few days to adjust to being back home, where the peace and quiet was bliss compared to the constant necessary noises of the monitors which now seemed like a distant memory. I found it most comfortable to sleep sat upright in the armchair with my left leg up on a stool, and this would be the case for the next few months. I had everything I needed to close to hand; I was set. I am fortunate that I had family and friends around me to help, they were golden. I didn't have to worry about anything other than to concentrate on getting stronger. If you're a dog lover you will understand this, if not then go get yourself a pooch; they are the best, trust me on this. Our family dog was a red Staffordshire bullterrier answering to the name Banjo. From the first moment I arrived home, he never once left my side. He would rest his head on my good leg and just look at me. He knew I was ill and psychologically still way down compared to my normal self. That's the thing with dogs, they are the best listeners in the world and you can tell them anything, pour out your heart and soul, share your deepest thoughts and emotions, and they'll never let you down or betray you, they'll love you unconditionally. Banjo was a bigger part of my psychological recovery than most. He sadly passed a few years ago. I miss him still.

A couple of weeks went past, I was adjusting to life as a 'cabbage survivor' as we are known. Coronary artery bypass grafts, make you a cabbage. I howled the first time I heard this, but as it goes, I am quite proud of my cabbage status. I was comfortable with the system I had devised for taking the required medication of which there was a cartload at this stage. I had also taken it upon myself to start reading up on the types of foods that would best aid my recovery, and long-term be beneficial to my heart condition. I figured, this was now life-long and I owed it to the consultants, nurses and all the staff who had worked so hard to save me, to give everything my best shot. I did not intend to live like a monk, but in the main to be sensible and get clued up in order to give myself the best, long-term chances. My knowledge prior to the blip about heart disease was pretty much zero, so I also began to read anything and everything I could, to try to understand what had happened to me and why. I wanted to know about the long term prognosis and anything that I could pick up on to give me a basic knowledge of my now life-long, condition. I wanted to be able to hold a reasonable, structured conversation with my consultant, nurses and doctor so that I could engage in and understand what my treatment, recovery and rehabilitation was about. I am no expert by any stretch of the imagination, but I felt I owed it to these good people and myself to make the effort. The physical stuff I knew: I could work like a dog, that was the easy part in my mind, so I studied as best I could, gradually finding a basic level of knowledge and understanding. I am so glad I made the effort to do this and I advise anyone to learn about their condition whatever that may be. If you have even a basic knowledge it does help and maybe also helps your consultants, doctors and nurses to help you that little bit easier. Food for thought perhaps?

It was middle of July, the weather was glorious, as you would expect at that time of year, long warm-to-hot sunny days, generally feel good weather as I like to call it. The family and I had decided to head down south to sunny Dorset for a week or, to be more precise, to Weymouth. I think most people have that one place, or maybe a couple, where they just feel at ease and enjoy being there for no particular reason other than it feels right. For me it's Weymouth. I have spent a lot of time there over the years. As a family we were regulars, down there a few times a year when my now-very-grown-up daughters were little, lots of good happy memories. I was looking forward to making the trip. I still couldn't move around to far maybe a few hundred metres on a good day but I figured, if I took it steady I would be fine, I could sit in deck chair and eat ice cream with the best of them. It was arranged; the whole family loaded up the convoy of vehicles it would take to get three generations of us down there and off we went, me riding shot gun, it was a strange feeling because I had never been driven before. I imagined this is how it would feel to be sat on the back of a tandem maybe? Anyway, I didn't care; we were all set, all together and happily on our way.

My favorite part of any journey heading south is to reach the bridge spanning the estuary at Avonmouth. We place our bets on the approach; it is high stakes and the tension is unbelievable: will it be tide in or tide out? The cheers of victory for those who call it correctly are loud and cut you to the very bone if, like me on the vast majority of occasions, you call it wrong. Made me smile looking behind to see similar celebrations and indeed commiserations going on in the rest of our convoy. How much fun can you have crossing a bridge, I ask you? Give it a go next time you're heading south on the M5, good clean fun.

Once over the estuary, I feel as though my normal life is lifted from me in some way and I slip blissfully into holiday mode. On we go, sunshine and blue skies, everyone looking forward to the break away. We wave and roar at big 'Arnold Carass' as he is known to us, some of you will have seen him I am sure: the huge wicker running man alongside the motorway. We peel off at Junction 25, heading through beautiful rolling countryside and quaint villages, then the first glimpses of the sea appear and the cheers go up again. Maybe it's a landlocked Black Country thing, but I find there is something very magical about catching your first sight of the ocean. I often wonder if those born and raised by the sea appreciate how lucky they are. I hope that they do, I like to believe this is the case.

At last we pull off the dual track and its windows all the way down to let that sea air in, trundling along the marina looking at the boats, the sound of the seagulls filling the skies above. Now I understand the seagulls are not loved by everyone and, yes, they poo on your car and your nice clean shirt, they nick your chips and ice creams, scare your kids, generally deafen you all day on the beach. All I can say is this: if you don't like it don't go. Go somewhere else, it's their home and we are their guests. It wouldn't be the same without them. I love them anyway.

Our accommodation for the week had unspoiled views over the fleet, Chesil beach, and out across the ocean beyond. The breeze, of which there is always plenty in Weymouth, gently cooled the patio area, also taking the heat of the room down to a comfortable temperature, it was perfect, just what was needed at this point. It had been a hard month on us all as a family. I felt happy with the situation and was looking forward to our week in the sun.

There are a few basic rules in our family when it comes to Weymouth, most of which revolve around naughty treats, I say 'naughty' depending on whether you have a heart condition to look after or not. First night there, without question, it's fish and chips, lashings of salt and vinegar, ice-cold cans of fully leaded coke, sat on the harbor wall looking at the boats, something we love. It's just one of those moments. This time however, as I sat and smiled inside, I paused for a moment or two and looked at my family who were laughing and joking, reminiscing of old times spent there, doing just as we were now, enjoying the fish and chips. I could see my girls, now young women full of life but also sat there as little girls full of the devil, but in such a good way. I had loved every second spent there with them over the years and I now felt a whole new depth of appreciation for those bygone days, and indeed for the present. It started to dawn on me just how fortunate I was to still be alive and savoring that precious moment. My fish and chips had never tasted so good. You can keep your fancy restaurants; fish and chips, can of coke, Weymouth harbor, it just doesn't get any better than that.

The sun gods shined down on us all week long. It was truly glorious, visiting lots of favorite places and doing lots of our favorite things. I did so miss being able to swim though. My scars were healing well to be fair, but the stiches and staples in my leg dictated that I couldn't use the pool or go in the sea, although I will admit to putting my right foot in the ocean. I am sorry but you cannot go to the coast without getting your toes wet, just no. We sat on the rocks at Portland bill, eating the world's biggest Mr Softie ice cream (another family rule) watching the waves crash over the rocks, the taste of the salty spray on our lips, free as the seagulls that filled the skies above us, or so it felt to me. The days were long and we made the most of them. I was ribbed blind by my daughters for having to sit in the shaded shelters on the esplanade with the all the old folk -

I was referred to as a 'sleeper', sat there dozing, leaning on my walking stick.

Our time passed so quickly. Towards the end of the week I went down to the beach around 6:30 am with my daughter who wanted to jog around the bay a run of about six miles in total. I was happy to sit on the sand in the early-morning sun and I watched her disappear round the bay, the dog stretched out on the sand by my side in comfort. Is it me or do dogs know how to make any sleep look good?

I took in the fresh air off the ocean, filling my lungs slowly although it was still very uncomfortable to take in a full capacity, but I was getting a little better each day, I thought. I looked around the bay, out across the hills and rugged Jurassic coastline beyond, the waves played their gentle backing vocals while they lapped the shore. Even the seagulls seemed to lower their volume just a little for me to savor the moment. The beach was almost deserted apart from a couple of people with their dogs who were enjoying their freedom, splashing around in the sea. Reflecting on events of the last month or so, I felt fortunate to be there and so very grateful to be caught in this moment. I felt almost at peace, grateful to have spent this time with my family. I am sure we all appreciated it and, certainly, we had all needed it. As my old dad used to say: 'once you done it, they can't take it off you.' He was right about that.

The week came to a close and we headed home with some happy memories. Time is so precious; boy did I know this more than ever before.

Every year for three weeks in July, the Tour de France has captivated me from a little kid right up to the present day. I immerse myself in the pleasure and pain world of the professional peloton, (the name given to the main group of cyclists in a race) hurtling at breakneck speeds around France. I love the intrigue of the chess-like game that is played out daily between the teams to get their GC rider (team leader) or sprinter into position for that much coveted stage victory or overall grand-tour win. Cycling is very much a team sport: for every GC rider there are eight or nine guys who kill themselves daily, riding themselves into the ground to put their GC man into yellow or green or polka dots, depending on the objectives of that team within the tour. I don't care how strong or talented you are as a cyclist, without a strong bunch of guys behind you, willing to sacrifice themselves for you, you will achieve and win very little, if anything. All the greats or giants of the road as they are known have one thing in common: great teams behind them.

A good friend of mine nicknamed Digger had come to see me. To give you an idea about him, Digger and I had done a fair amount of cycling together, most notably for me the time we embarked on a crazy ride starting out in fort William up in bonnie Scotland, covering a very hilly six hundred miles down to the capital in the heart of London - over six days, you do the maths. It was a real pleasure-and-pain experience; we rode in some foul weather almost every day, wind, rain, long hard miles in the saddle. I was along on this ride to act as a domestique, (a rider who works for the benefit of his or her team leader), to ride at the front all day to protect Digger from as much of the wind and weather in general as possible, so that he could save energy. Digger had run in the Fort William marathon on the Sunday and on the Monday morning we had set off on our six-hundred-mile journey to London - and the following Sunday Digger would be running the London marathon.

My point is this the man is a machine. His powers of endurance are something pretty special and how he ran a full marathon either side of a grueling six days and six hundred miles in the saddle I will never know. By the time we arrived in London I was shot, tank emptied; I could not have walked twenty-six feet never mind run twenty-six miles, but Digger did – that is the measure of the man. Bearing all this in mind, it came as no shock whilst we sat talking of my plans to do a ride of some kind on the first anniversary of my heart blip, that Digger was up for it.

'Count me in,' he said, no hesitation.

As it happened, we were watching that day's stage of the Tour de France, to be precise the mountain stage, which finished at the summit of Mont Ventoux, or, as it affectionately referred to by the locals of the area, 'the Giant of Provence'. The Giant is one of, if not the most, feared and revered mountain stages on the Tour, in fact any grand tour, even by the pros. It is high, steep, painfully brutal and totally unforgiving, more a war of attrition to reach the summit than a ride. It's famous in cycling circles, one of the holy grails if you like, along with Alpe d'Huez, Col du Tourmalet, and a few select others. The Ventoux is a mountain that puts fear in the legs of any cyclist. We watched the race leader's yellow jersey majestically power up the mighty Ventoux and Digger and I exchanged, how shall I say, a certain look, and then it was said out loud what we had both been thinking. I will hand credit to Digger for the suggestion, but I was sold on the idea before the words had even left his lips.

'How about the Mont Ventoux mate? That would be something.'

Instantly, I had butterfly's in the pit of my stomach but I was grinning like a kid at Christmas. 'Let's do it, that's the one, it's on.'

There, in that moment, the idea was born and set in stone: 9th June 2014, exactly a year to the day after my heart blip, the target would be the mighty 'Giant of Provence', Mont Ventoux. To quote Digger, it would be a 'doozey' and I couldn't argue with that.

I was filled with child-like enthusiasm, my adrenaline was pumping at this crazy idea. As outlandish as it might seem to target arguably the toughest climb in cycling, it just felt right. I don't know why but it felt as though, in that moment, destiny had come calling and it had given me the date in advance and now the place to crown the upcoming battle that lay in front of me, in the shape of the baron, harsh landscape of the slopes leading to the summit of the mighty Ventoux. Would we make it? Time would tell; it was all there to focus on and aim for now.

Over the next few days my thoughts were dominated by the adventure that lay ahead. I spent a long time reading up on the Ventoux; of course, being a cycling fan, I had seen many stages battled out on the torturous slopes, of tours won and lost. I knew of its history going way back to the early tours. I wanted to know more: what did the pros think about it, past and present? how did they approach the climb? what gears they used? what amounts of food and water were necessary to fuel the body enough whilst on the bike to reach the summit? I was looking to educate myself in every detail possible. Mont Ventoux has such a fearsome and unforgiving reputation I didn't want to leave anything to chance. I am a great believer that cycling is as much about being psychologically prepared as physically, maybe even more so. You can have the strongest engine and all the talent in the world, but without psychological strength to match it becomes almost useless. In my current physical state, it was not possible to work on my fitness, that was all still to come, so I focused on resting, eating right, and studying all I could about what I now felt was my mountain to climb. I accepted it was a big ask and the outcome far from certain, but that was what drove me on: to prove to myself I could do it, that my time on the bike wasn't over. Filled with excitement, apprehension and admittedly a certain amount of doubt, I relished the idea and enormity of the challenge, embracing it the only way I knew how, all in. Rightly or wrongly, that's the way I am built - all or nothing. So I read and learnt and the more I read, the more I fell in love with the whole adventure.

I had spoken to Big George, and in typical Big George fashion, directly after saying he thought I was crazy and it was a mad idea, he said 'I'm up for this let's do it,' and then came the immortal words: 'It's just a hill, a big hill! But just a hill, we will get up it.'

Big George has a very simple philosophy when it comes to training and cycling in general. The formula is beautifully simple: time and distance in the saddle - that's it, there is no substitute for it. Primitive and basic as this sounds in today's world of scientifically based training methods, I do buy into this method and, believe me, when Big George has you in the hurt locker on your limits, five hours and a hundred miles at a time, on any terrain, who can argue? It was around this time I also spent a nice time chatting with my friend Stig. Yes, we all have odd nicknames. He is a lifelong cycling fan and well versed in the history of our crazy sport; he is also very useful on the bike, has a big engine and has bags of that dig-in-and-suffer attitude, as would become massively evident later on. He was instantly fired up by the idea of riding the Mont Ventoux. He had previously ridden the Alpe d'Huez and Galibier and he was keen to add the Giant of Provence to his Palmares. Our band of brothers was growing and I was happy to have Stig on board.

At this stage, although I was aware of the size of the challenge I was taking on, what I wasn't aware of was how unfit I had become and, physically, just how far I was from getting back on the bike at all. Big George too, as I have said, had not cycled in three years himself. These things I hadn't really considered in too much depth because I was swept along in the Romance of the idea. I had almost forgotten that my heart had gone through a massive trauma, indeed it had yet to be tested beyond short walks of no more than a few hundred metres at a time. Was it too much to assume I could just get back on the bike and pedal it? Being stubborn, driven, and having something to focus on is all well and good, but in the back of my mind, in the darkest corner and hiding away, was the devil, which is doubt, the little 'what if' question I had no answer to. I would sit and debate this with myself in my own mind. I needed to start trying to push myself and, not knowing how to best attempt this, I was getting frustrated trying to find the answer, and then it literally dropped on the door mat by way of a letter from the cardiology consultant at Russell's Hall Hospital. I was due to attend early on in August for a follow-up appointment and treadmill test. This gave me renewed enthusiasm. It felt as though I was on the verge of taking the next step. Feeling a lot better, I was up for putting my patched-up heart to the test and very much looking forward to it. I didn't know it then, but the gateway I very much needed to set me free on the long road ahead was about to open. The hard miles were about to begin and there would be many of them.

5

Wrestles chimp at 1000/1

August arrived and all was still sunny. I had been increasing my physical activities, progressing as much as I felt comfortable with, albeit laps around the garden, walking up and down the stairs in intervals, increasing how far I would walk up and down the street. I found the heat seemed to affect me far more than pre blip and fatigue would hit me like a freight train with no slow build-up of felling tired, or signs of running out of steam gradually, as I had felt before; it was now sudden and overwhelming, and all part of a massive learning curve I was about to become aware of. I continued with my self-prescribed cardio rehabilitation through early August. At times psychologically, I would become frustrated at how little I could do as I couldn't help but compare the post-blip me with the pre-blip version of myself; we were a million miles apart, there was no denying the fact or kidding myself. I guess I had gone as far as I could unaided, so when the day arrived for my first follow-up meeting with the consultant, I was so relieved and so ready.

I had agreed to take part in a drug trial during my initial period in Russell's Hall Hospital with the consultant who had basically saved my life and taken care of me during those early days pre-New Cross, Dr Barr. On arrival at the cardiology department, I was to report directly to his team. Walking down the corridor, I was greeted by smiling faces of the staff; some I recognized, some I was not so sure about but the amazing and very humbling thing was they all remembered me, calling me by name, asking how I was getting on I was so impressed by the fact, a very humbling experience. Feeling slightly apprehensive and unsure what to expect, a brief wait followed the knock on the consulting-room door. Any nerves or apprehension I had subsided almost immediately, the room had that jovial light-hearted feel about it, I was greeted by the sister nurses who would take care of me during the trial period, their whole approach was friendly and relaxed which put me at ease, genuinely nice people and so passionate about what they did was my impression and time would prove my assumptions correct. My height, weight and blood-pressure was taken, also a blood test. By now I was used to needles and having blood work done. I smiled and laughed a little as the pre-needle warning 'sharp scratch' was given. The nurses had a good sense of humor and we had a fair few laughs along the way. From there we went to meet Dr Barr. On my walking into the room, he stood up and shook my hand. It was there that I was first able to put a figure on the odds of survival I had faced at the start - Dr Barr referred to me as his '1000/1 shot'. This has stayed with me to this day and I'm certain will continue to do so and I am quite proud of these odds. We discussed the trial in general. In my basic terminology, it was research into lowering cholesterol in the blood, also my recovery and rehabilitation. I was very impressed with this man. His knowledge and sheer enthusiasm were quite captivating. We laughed as he recalled that he had been impressed by the fact that I had got up and made my bed with military precision the morning after coming around from the coma, I was the more impressed that he had noticed.

I was proud that he said that my cycling and fitness had gone a long way to contributing to my survival of the heart blip and, at forty-one I had been fairly young too. Any older or less fit and I probably would not have survived - there had been considerable damage to my heart and the mi had left a lot of scarring. But as a muscle my heart was quite large, I like to think due to cycling most of my life and it therefore stood up to the trauma, hence my 1000/1 odds of survival. The whole conversation was a pleasure, very informative yet light-hearted too. I have enormous respect for this man and his team.

I had been referred to Action Heart, which is a specialist cardiology rehabilitation unit, which, fortunately for me, is based within the same hospital. Before I could attend however, I was required to undergo a treadmill test. Ordinarily this would be a straight forward test for me, so as the nurse with her ever-present Colgate smile took me down to the test room, I could feel my adrenaline starting to flow; I felt this would be another step closer to getting back on the bike. The nurse wished me good luck and left me in the capable hands of the physiotherapists who would carry out the testing. Once changed into running shoes and shorts, I was ready. The room was quite chilly but this turned out to be a good thing; sticky backed pads were attached to my chest area and wrists in various places in turn hooking me up to an ECG and blood-pressure monitor, which unsettled me a bit as the noise took me back to my darkest of days in the icu unit with all its noises and lights. Taking a deep breath, I managed to get hold of myself. I admit to this day I have a hard time psychologically being in and around hospitals since the blip, and similar noises made by those of the monitors in the icu take me straight back there in my head. Sometimes it's worse than others but it's always the same. Certain noises trigger it off. It's a long slow coping process but I am working on it.

The test was medically about monitoring, measuring my heart function and blood pressure whilst under load, gradually increasing from a slow walking pace on a flat level, increasing the speed and percentage gradient every two minutes. The increase in my BPM (Beats Per Minute) and BP (Blood Pressure) being constantly monitored. There was also some clever function of working out my lung capacity and percentage of the oxygen I was processing from the intake of air. All this was way beyond my understanding, for me it was simply about pushing myself a little bit if I could to see for myself where my fitness levels and capabilities were at.

The physios explained everything to me in detail. I took it all in as best I could, but I just wanted to get on with it. Then the magic happened. It was suggested to me that, when I felt I had enough, to say so and the test would end or, in the unlikely event I was still going longer than they needed me to, they would stop me. My inner chimp was instantly going ballistic. 'Unlikely' - he wasn't happy at all! Don't get me wrong, I wasn't offended or insulted in any way, on the contrary this gave me the spark, the motivation, to smash it as we say.

The first few minutes felt good, a stretch, a warmup almost, a nice gentle walk, no problem. I was fine. At six minutes in, I began to notice the gradient a bit more, six percent I was still walking but starting to work. My BPM was climbing steadily and BP was fine.

'You're doing well, John. Keep it going.'

Indeed, on we went. My fire was well alight now. As the gradient and speed increased so did my BPM. I was working hard now, the sweat giving way to the force of gravity running down my head onto my chest and beyond. My left leg was beginning to burn, sternum screaming at me in pain, no way was I stopping yet, heart pounding away like a drop-forge hammer but it felt ok to me and the physios gave constant encouragement. I figured I would push myself to destruction, I was in the right place after all. I felt safe there, putting my complete faith in the physios taking care of me. Ten percent and climbing now, jogging to keep pace with the treadmill, then twelve percent, deep into my ability to suffer, thighs burning, heart trying to burst out of my ribcage, every breath was agony.

Certain my sternum was about to split wide open, focused on a drawing pin stuck in the wall in front of me, the monitors were going crazy, thirteen minutes in.

'John, this is excellent. You can stop anytime you want to now.'

'No way! Don't you dare!' The chimp was screaming at me again. Every muscle and sinew in my body wished me to stop and I was willing the physios to stop me and end the torture but I simply couldn't; I would have taken it as a failure to just pull up.

Tunnel vision closed in on me, the build-up of lactic in my legs turning them into lumps of wood. Struggling to get enough air in to meet the demand for oxygen my body required, I hit the red zone. I was shot, completely spent. Just as I was about to quit and admit failure - salvation!

'Stop now, John. That's enough.'

I will call this an even draw. In reality the physios could see I was on some futile trying-to-kill-myself mission and stepped in to stop me from doing so. I thank them for that; they were very understanding with me. The figures are unimportant; suffice to say that the physios and the consultant were pleased with the results - all relative to someone who had been through major heart surgery and was in the condition I was. Most importantly, I had been able to push myself and push hard, deep in the red zone, and not break, gaining confidence and the psychological boost I needed to push on.

I was due to start the cardio-rehabilitation program with Action Heart four days later. Having pushed myself so hard, it took the whole four days to recover properly. To put this in perspective, pre-blip after an effort of this intensity I would have easily recovered and been good to go again the next day. Clearly those days were long gone but this had been a massive step forward; I felt good. A short debrief with Dr Barr followed, follow-up appointments were booked in. Feeling positive, I was looking forward to getting stuck into the rehabilitation at Action Heart in a few days. Things were all good.

'Impressive', was my first thought on walking through the double doors that led to the gym area within the Action Heart centre, a light airy room, very clean open feel to it, maybe sixty metres by forty metres with what can be described as a small running track in the middle. A sea of cardio-based exercise machines, treadmills, spin-bikes, rowing machines, cross-trainers, steppers. It was a good multi-gym with various weights machines and free weights; you name it, this gym had it. Grinning to myself, I had a good feeling about the place. I immediately felt comfortable in those surroundings. After a guided tour it was explained to me that I would attend three times that week, following a program specifically designed to meet the needs of my condition and my current level of recovery and fitness. I would be mentored by a member of the Action Heart team who would closely monitor my heart rate, blood pressure, general well-being. Any necessary adjustments would be made to my program as we went along. Training would be within the limits of my BPM and over time this would be increased, depending on my fitness gains and rehabilitation progress in general. Due to attend for a whole year with constant review and assessment, I felt I was in very good hands. This was perfect for me, exactly what I needed. I couldn't wait to get started.

The facilities were excellent, the staff all knowledgeable and specialists in the field of cardio-rehabilitation and sports physiology. There were also nutritionists, psychotherapists, anything you could think of was there and available at any time. A series of lectures, which I was expected to attend as part of the program, fitted in perfectly with my thirst for the knowledge I craved to understand better my heart condition and the rehabilitation, recovery process. The lectures were very informative and I learnt a great deal. My understanding of risk factors, causes, cures, of coronary disease grew immensely. I learnt a lot about the types of diet and nutrition that would benefit me now post-blip, making changes and tweaks to my already clean diet had a big beneficial effect.

I learned about sleep deprivation and was shocked by just how bad this can be for you, having spent many years of my working life on long night shifts and working unsocial hours, the clues were there. Also, stress, what a silent but deadly contributor this can be. We are all aware no doubts of the obvious no no's: smoking, drinking, poor diet, lack of exercise, all major risk factors but for me personally, and I stress I am no expert, poor rest and sleep deprivation over the years and stress in my daily life, were, I believe, the major contributors to my downfall. I would advise anyone to take just a few minutes; be honest with yourself, think about your lifestyle on a daily basis, make those changes no matter how small or large. Any help you give your body, trust me it will thank you long term. I learned the hard way, believe me I would not wish it on anyone, it's no fun.

My first session in the gym was mainly about setting the program to my current levels. Let's just say that my perceived level and the reality of where I was, were very different. From the start it was clear I had a mountain to climb in rehabilitation before I could realistically get back on my bike and cycle up Mont Ventoux. A mountain for a mountain seemed about right.

The physio was a good lad, very switched on and enthusiastic; we hit it off straight away. Our conversation moved from why I was there to cycling, which he was impressively knowledgeable about, and skiing which I knew very little about. He was an instructor and had spent a lot of time in the French Alps during winter time, the same regions that are used in the Tour de France during summer time, so you can imagine we had plenty to talk about while I worked my way around my various stations at the gym. I was in a good place; I was feeling happy and enjoying my time.

My program was roughly mapped out during that first session, which took a couple of hours. I had used various pieces of cardio-based equipment, no weights for me at this stage. The rowing was absolute agony for my chest, but I was willing to give it a go and include this in my program, albeit in small doses. Treadmill, cross-trainer I was fine, the cherry on the cake, I would be allowed to use the spin bike. Normally I would consider spin bikes - exercise bikes or rollers - which I do use indoors I admit, as nothing more than a tool to warm up and warm down. There is no substitute for the real thing, sorry there just isn't, my opinion anyway. All that aside and given my present condition and the events that bought me to this moment, to be able to climb aboard this thing vaguely resembling a bike was enough to put a wide grin on my face and a lump in my throat. It was the first time my butt had sat on a saddle in over two months and, boy, did it feel good. I was only allowed to pedal for three minutes, pathetic I know, but nothing on this earth could have bought those three minutes off me. As I turned my legs, I felt another little piece of the load remove itself from my back. I was making progress, baby steps maybe but progress none the less.

Two days later I returned to the action heart gym. My program had been worked out in detail, based off my initial session. I was happy with it so - let the come-back begin. My program for the next couple of months would run the same, starting with blood pressure, resting pulse taken and logged; then a warm up and stretching session which was structured and had to be followed rigidly, most important in any training so I was fully on board with this; next my circuits, of which there were three, involving three-minute efforts on treadmill, cross trainer, rowing machine, spin bike, and with one walking lap of the track in between each exercise for recovery; then step-up block, high knee raises, and twenty sit-ups and crunches. Ok, I admit it doesn't sound much, but in my then condition it worked me hard and it was non-stop and pretty intense. The warm-down at the end mirrored the warm-up: blood pressure and resting pulse recorded again. I was to wear a heart-rate monitor the whole time and record it after each effort. The aim for those first few weeks was to train at 120 bpm and, if it climbed above, I had to ease off but work hard enough to maintain it. A new concept, although basic this was very science-in-sports to me. I had come from a competitive cycling background at a time when training was basically, get on the bike and pedal it as hard, fast, long as you could, when you were dying a thousand deaths, totally spent, you did some more. A far cry from the modern and scientific methods of today.

I was enjoying this new, or at least new to me approach, well, up to a point. My inner chimp was not at all amused with these new controlled methods; he is, and I am certain will always be, old school. At times he got the better of us and we had moments of madness, but generally I played ball, doing as I was told. The program was enough to work me hard without killing me or putting me in the red. I could feel the efforts, sure it was uncomfortable, painful at times especially around the sternum, which was pure agony when rowing, but I sucked it up as best I could and kept quiet.

After a couple of weeks, I began to notice the changes: general fitness was improving, recovery was quicker, I felt stronger, I was having to work harder to hit my target heart rate, all good signs that my three sessions a week were paying dividends. All this was fueling my enthusiasm and drive to reach for the bike again. This was way off but it felt like I was getting there. It was good to get a sweat on again; I love that feeling post work-out after the showers, your whole body, tingling, that boom. I feel alive, light on my feet, feeling sharp; it's a good feeling. I was beginning to feel like my old self in some ways, yet different in others, I knew deep down I would never feel quite the same again, but for now I was feeling ok.

August ended. I felt it had been a good month in my recovery, progressing from being only able to walk a few hundred metres, to training three times a week. Heading into September my confidence building that I would soon be able to consider the bike again, my fitness, core strength improving steadily; I was pleased with progress. Still the biggest problem physically was the sternum, which gave me so much pain whilst training and constant discomfort daily, but I figured it just needed time, after all it had only been three months since the surgery.

Outside of training, my problem was sleeping. I still sat up in the armchair and I had not been able to sleep in a bed since the surgery. I still couldn't bear to lay down because the pain from the sternum wouldn't allow it. Averaging no more than three hours sleep a night, most of which was broken, getting quality sleep was a real problem. These issues aside, generally I felt I was doing ok.

During the many hours spent at the Action Heart gym I would watch my fellow hearties, this is the name I affectionately gave to my rehabilitation comrades, of whom there were many. I am a great people watcher, a student of human moves so to speak. I think sometimes you can learn more about a person by their actions as opposed to what they say. I recalled how Dr Barr had said that at forty-one I was young to have suffered a mi on the scale I had. This was never more evident to me than in the Action Heart gym. With the odd exception, the vast majority of the hearties were in their sixties, seventies and beyond. I guess I must have stood out a little, often the object of a surprised look that said, 'what are you doing in here?' - which was ok; I didn't mind. My qualifying credentials were there for all to see. The scar running the full length of my inner left leg was still highly visible at this stage, about a cm thick and rose-red, my membership badge; we all have them in the hearties club, some more than others. In my opinion badges of honour and pride, that say we are the lucky ones, we made it.

I consider myself fortunate to have ended up at Action Heart. This may sound bizarre, I appreciate, given the events that put me there, but without them I would never have met the people I did. They were from all walks of life: race, gender, religious beliefs, all completely irrelevant, we were all just hearties. I met and talked to so many different people, from high-flying business people, to medical professionals, factory workers, teachers, housewives, single parents, people with huge families and social circles, people with no one so that their only social contact was us hearties, former sports people and those who had never done anything remotely sporty until now at Action Heart. My point is, we were all so different yet all the same, united by our condition. Everyone got on well and I can confidently say we were all friends. They were lovely people and it was an honour to spend time amongst them. I wish them well.

The training continued and my three sessions a week were really paying off. I was improving and feeling strong. However, as the end of September loomed large on the calendar, I could feel the frustration building inside me. The clock was ticking, I was becoming impatient, the days passed and my frustrations grew. A year to get ready for Mont Ventoux, it had seemed like plenty of time way back at the start of July, but now, almost into October, I still hadn't as much as looked at the bike, which was still under its sheet in the shed. I needed to get riding and soon. For now, all I could do was keep on with the program, be a slave to the heart-rate monitor that kept me and the inner chimp in check, for now at least. We were getting restless. Being honest with myself, I knew it was only a matter of time before I would crack; something had to give.

6

Back in the saddle

As September gave way to October, my frustration at not yet being back on the bike was increasing by the day. In the back of my mind I had eight months in which to train for and be ready to take on Mont Ventoux. It had been four months since I last cycled and any cyclist will tell you this is a huge amount of time to be off the bike. The training required to get back to the level you were at before a lay-off like this, is equally as huge. Even taking into account my time in the rehabilitation gym, I knew I had a massive number of hard miles and long hours in the saddle in front of me, if I was going to be fit and ready in time the following June. Factor into this scenario the potential for a bad winter, where heavy frosts, ice, dare I say even snow, would slow training right down, and in extreme conditions force me off the road and onto the poor alternative of indoor trainers. These thoughts weighing heavy in mind, my mood was deteriorating fast. Getting ratty and angry with myself, my frustration was beginning to boil over into my rehabilitation sessions also. In short, little Joe, my inner chimp, had lost his rag; tired and impatient he was getting the better of me.

Those closest to me had noticed the changes in my mood; my frustrations were plain to see. I had talked it out with family and staff at Action Heart and it was agreed that I could train at 140 bpm an increase of 20 bpm and also do a fourth circuit on top of my usual three. Whilst I appreciated the increase and step-up in training and intensity, deep down I knew this wasn't going to help for long. I am my own worst enemy at times, I admit this, my patience was running out fast. I tried for about a week to remain focused on the newly increased limits of the program and to keep control but I knew it was a lost cause. I was battling little Joe every second in the gym. Flexing his muscles, losing his temper, he was and probably still is the strongest part of me and in the end he won. I cracked and gave in to the rise of the chimp. He was back and there would be no stopping him now.

Monday rolled round, as I walked the mile from my home to Action Heart within the hospital. I had taken to walking there and back as part of the warm-up and warm-down I could feel the bad mood I was in running through my system like the disease it is. Being stubborn and fired up is all well and good and not a bad thing when channeled and used in the right way but the down side to this: if you have no outlet for it, it can be a curse, as I say, like a disease, robbing you of the ability to think straight, be pleasant, turning you in to a morose, grumpy lump and certainly not much fun to be around. I guess I owe a lot of people an apology for being this way on occasions. It wasn't all sunshine and roses. I had my dark days and plenty of them and I am lucky to have family and friends who could see past this and the reasons why. They could see the journey I was on physically and psychologically, which, looking back, was probably the hardest part for me and to this day still is. The whole blip and journey thus far had taken far more out of me than I realized. I found it difficult to accept what had happened, the changes, the limitations that events had forced on me. It was just hard yakka as we say.

I am not sure how long I had been sat on the spin bike gently warming up, I don't recall arriving at the gym, having bp taken, stretching or any of the usual routine. I just kind of came out of the frustration-daze I had been in; a light sweat had formed on my brow, so my guess it took quite a while. First circuit completed I was in a bad mood; I just wasn't feeling it at all. I apologize now to all those people who cared for me, advised, supported me for what followed. The chimp took over: I just went with it. The next three circuits I simply hammered it, pushing as hard as I could on every piece of equipment, in between as many sit-ups as I could do plus the walking lap instead of the normal twenty, the heart-rate monitor going ballistic. I won't reveal the figure it hit, suffice to say it was way above my allowed limits. In full self-destruct mode, I just wanted to push and push hard. I finished on the spin bike as always, pedaling that thing so hard I wanted to turn the pedals off it, shatter the bearings, blow it apart. The sweat running out of me gathered in a growing pool on the floor, as it ran off me down the spin bike. Into the last set of sit-ups; God only knows how many I did, pushing on until my core just wouldn't lift me anymore. I was on fire, my whole body screaming at me to stop; I hit the red zone; I was cooked and sat on a gym mat slumped in a heap exhausted. The chimp was strutting about inside me like King Kong, pleased with himself. Having had the time of his life, he was happy at least. The other more measured side of me was already thinking, 'what the hell was all that about you idiot.' Christ, I hope no one saw that.

How stupid and disrespectful of me to think it would have gone unnoticed. The staff were amazingly dedicated to our wellbeing, and ever vigilant to our activities, for our own safety and our own good. My strop, and basically that's what it was, a big boy's strop, had been closely monitored by the physios. They had the intelligence and compassion to allow me to vent off the steam of my frustrations in this way whilst keeping close eye on me, ready to step in and prevent me from killing myself. I was sitting there, feeling guilty and a little stupid, staring at the floor waiting for my jack hammer of a heart to calm down and return to something like a normal pulse rate, when a hand was gently placed on my sweaty forearm, with calming voice and the words, 'are you alright?'

Looking up slowly, feeling embarrassed and ashamed of myself, rightly so I admit, I was greeted by a very non-judgmental, smiling face.

'You were going a little bit crazy there for a while. Are you feeling ok?'

'Yeh, I'm fine, sorry about that.'

'Ok, well walk a few laps of the track, take on some water and go warm down.'

I apologized again and did as I was told, feeling like an oversized naughty schoolboy. I felt so much better for burning off some steam and with it the frustrations. The tradeoff was, I now felt, awful for throwing away all regard for my program in such a fashion. In the many sessions that would follow, I had long conversations and debates with the physio who had asked if I was ok. She became my voice of reason, helping me a lot with the constant battle to control the chimp. I look at this as the positive to come out of my negative outburst; in this sense it had been a good thing and maybe it had to happen in order for me to progress.

That night I gave the prospect of attempting to get back on the bike a lot of serious thought. It was a big step, physically and psychologically, and there were many doubts in my mind at this stage. In the end I just put my fears aside, figuring it was more a case of me needing to take a leap of faith and just get on it. Whatever was meant to be, would be. The next morning it was cold but dry outside. I wrapped up went out to the bike shed that I hadn't so much as looked at in months, let alone what lay inside. I don't know why, and I admit it's pretty silly really, I had butterflies in the stomach as I opened the door and looked across at the sheet covering my beloved trek road bike where it had been for the last four months. Pulling the sheet off her (yes, I know I know the bike is a 'she', they always are), I started to smile, saying out loud, 'and so we meet again, old friend'. Holding the bars in one hand I gave the saddle an affectionate tap with the other. To set the record straight, I don't have a strange fetish for bikes, I am just superstitious as are most cyclists. This particular bike was like a second skin to me. It is a cliché but when I ride, the bike and I are one and the same, the bike is an extension of me, that's as simple as I can explain it. My bike was not some all-singing all-dancing full-carbon pro-team replica, ten grands' worth, which you tend to see parked up outside any café on a Sunday morning with some middle-aged, full-team replica kitted out, team-Sky wanna-be weekend warrior, crowing about how light this is or how expensive that was, all the while stuffing a full English breakfast down their two or three stone overweight face - really! Oh yeh, there are lots of them out there. No, my trusty steed was just a bog-standard, off-the-shelf, alloy-framed item with carbon forks, 105 group set and wheels trek. Brand new you would get sufficient change for a good few coffees and cakes out of a thousand pounds. Let me tell you this, you can have a ten grand pro race bike or an entry-level like mine, they all have one thing in common: they aren't for looking at, they don't pedal themselves. Mine has done literally tens of thousands of miles and never lets me down. I use it all weathers, on all roads, mostly out in the countryside. Most rides it's covered in crap by the time I'm home. If you follow this simple philosophy, they last you: wash it, dry it, oil it, go again. I gave the old girl a good wipe down and check-over. She was good to go; more to the point, so was I.

Following my moment of madness two days earlier, I returned to Action Heart and the limits of my program. My new-found voice of restraint and reason came and chatted with me as I worked my way through the program. I told her of my plans to ride in the coming days, asking for her thoughts, opinions and advice on the subject. As a sports physiologist her input was of great value to me. I learnt and took a lot of what was given to me as good knowledgeable advice. I promised to wear the heart-rate monitor and make an effort to keep within a reasonable range. It was a big confidence-boost to me that, despite the real need for me to be sensible in my approach to the ride, she felt I was in a physical condition to get back on the bike. It was a good conversation. I made a few calls and the deal was done so to speak. I arranged to meet Digger at his flat in a couple of days and we would head out from there on a steady ride, just a gentle turn of the legs.

It was exactly four months since my heart blip, a very grey and cold-looking sky greeted me as I opened the curtains, a slight breeze but nothing to moan about, a damp drizzle in the air. That's the thing about cyclists: we are the world's greatest weather watchers; we study the weather like a master's degree student because we have to. If not, you can turn any ride into a complete disaster. It's all about the clothing choices you make - I am not talking fashion statements here either. It's critical to wear the correct amount of layers and the right type, to keep warm but not overheat, to keep cool but not become cold, to keep the wind out, to keep dry but not become soaked by your own sweat, hands. Feet, knees and ears are critically important to keep warm and dry. Temperature is vitally important to a cyclist;, being too hot is as bad as being too cold - and avoid getting soaked at all costs. Get it wrong you're in big trouble; with the right kit, you can pedal all day quite happily in any weather. My choices made, I loaded the bike on the rack, making the short drive to Digger's, my stomach still having that warm, porridge, honey-and-banana feel about it. This is my favorite go-to pre-ride breakfast and has been for years. It fuels me for a good two or three hours, fifty to sixty miles or there about. I always carry a few nuts, and oat-based bars in my cycling jersey pocket, or homemade flapjack made with honey as oppose to sugar. I'm not a big fan of energy gels to be honest but each to their own, whatever works for you, do it.

A welcome surprise was all set and waiting for me on my arrival. Digger had organized a little grupetto to accompany me on my first ride back. I smiled, it meant a lot to me that the lads were up for a ride out on such a cold wet and generally miserable October morning. The Stig was there with a wide grin, Rich Miles too, Rich has done some epic challenges, notably the Marathon des Sables with Digger a few years back. Likewise Rich is a real power-house on the bike, with a big engine. Also, my good friend Pat, whom I had cycled with many times. Pat is a very good cyclist, poetry in motion on the bike, he pedals perfect circles, giving the appearance of gliding along. Pat would probably argue this, but he is a lot better than he gives himself credit for in my opinion and also possessed that ability to dig in and suffer as was proven on the Cat & Fiddle sportive a few years back. It was a bitterly cold day, thirty-five miles in, we hit the seven miles of steep climbing to the summit at the Cat & Fiddle Inn, hence the name. Pat started to suffer at the foot of the climb but he dug in and ground it out at a decent pace too, despite his obvious pain and discomfort. On we rode; he put in a good shift. I was proud of him for his efforts; where a lot would have pulled up Pat kept going. Respect due, Chapeaux sir.

The mood was light, plenty of banter and micky-taking as we climbed aboard our trusty machines, rolling off down the hill that would lead our grupetto on its short journey through the village and out into the countryside beyond. I grinned to myself as my foot found its way into the clips on the pedals, locked in at last. It was good to feel the bars in my hands and the forward motion of the bike again. The cold wind and damp drizzle on my face had never felt so good. I had no expectations as to how I would feel getting back on the bike, in truth it's hard to describe, strange, almost surreal - and emotional, yes indeed. I felt good but mostly it was a bit blurred. Looking back, I don't believe it really sank in at the time just what a milestone it was on this crazy journey. I kind-of just got on the bike and rode it.

Heading out across the 'Mile Flat' as it's known locally, I felt the pressure, tension, frustrations, that had built up inside me in the weeks prior to this first ride, ease from my shoulders. Laughing and joking as we tootled along, just turning the legs, enjoying the ride together, up and over the hump-back bridge at the canal, sweeping right to the foot of Camp Hill. I had decided to go this way despite the boys' sensible suggestions to go around the other side and take the slightly flatter route. Camp Hill is maybe half-a-mile long; I am not sure how steep, nothing major but enough to get your heart working a bit. I needed to test myself, after all, this was no spin bike in the comfort of the gym; this was the real deal out on the road in the wind and rain. Suitably told off by the boys for making us all climb, up we went, nice and steady, left leg on fire every pedal stroke, heart rate up a fair bit higher than normal on a climb such as this.

I could definitely feel the four months' lay off and the fair dose of trauma I had been through since my last ride; positives - I was back in the saddle, pedaling again. Yes, it was painfully slow, nowhere near my old self, in reality a million miles away from being ready to attempt Mont Ventoux. Today none of that mattered in the slightest to me or anyone else, it was just a pleasure to be out on the bike with a great bunch of lads, laughing and enjoying the ride. I appreciated how fortunate I was to be there, in my mind I gave thanks for it.

Winding our way out and around the old airfield on a nice little circuit ridden hundreds of times before over the years, we maybe rode a little over twenty miles in all that day, just a nice stretch of the legs. Despite the cold and wet we had laughed, joked and loved every minute of the ride, warming up over a hot cup of tea on our return, we laughed a bit more. I will be forever in debt to the lads for making the first ride back such a genuine pleasure. It will stay in the memory for ever and a day. Thank you.

My voice of reason in the gym, and by now good friend, discussed how the ride had gone during the usual cardio-rehabilitation session the following day: comparing my heart rate numbers out on a real bike to the spin bikes in the gym, how I had felt, my recovery times and so on, in short a thorough debrief of the ride and the effects on me. We were both pleased with the results from a cardio-rehabilitation perspective. I explained my plan to ride a couple of times a week in between my cardio-program sessions, which was a big step up on my physical demands but, managed properly, she felt it could be done. I promised to ease up if I felt I was overdoing things, over-training was a massive 'no'.

In stark contrast to the previous ride, the morning was bright and sunny with clear blue skies, bitterly cold but a lovely day none the less. Trundling along through country lanes with a good friend of mine, the smell of autumn filling the chilly air as we rolled along, chatting about the events of the previous months, with all the ifs, buts and maybes said events had thrown up.

The ride was great, just a nice steady roll out but I felt loose and easy on the bike, comfortable considering, apart from the sternum which, as always, was the constant, painful reminder of the trauma my body had been through, and my now cabbage status. Eventually we pulled up at a café and, being so cold, we chose the hot soup of the day and bread-roll option. It was a good choice, instantly hitting the spot, warming us up a treat. The conversation moved on to my planned attempt on the mighty Mont Ventoux. Laughing, my friend accused me of being insane and rightly so, but also gave my confidence a huge boost by saying, 'you will do it, you're too stubborn not to.' We finished our soup and had a steady ride back. The whole ride was no more than twenty-five miles, but we talked the whole way and it helped me a great deal, getting a lot off my mind. An invaluable part of my psychological recovery, it most definitely lightened my load. Another great ride and good conversation.

Almost halfway through October it felt like at last I was really starting to get somewhere, doing three good sessions a week in the Acton Heart gym and now a couple of good rides under my belt. I made the sensible decision not to ride during the third week of October as there were heavy frosts. Normally this wouldn't stop me, but I simply couldn't risk crashing with my sternum basically held together with metal coils, the bone not fully healed to the point it could take an impact from crashing. I continued to train in the gym under the watchful eyes of my physio who kindly agreed to me increasing my time on the spin bike. During that week I made the call to Big George. He was up-beat and pleased to hear that I had been out a couple of times and turned my legs a little bit. We discussed the prospect of riding the next week or as soon as the frosts lifted. Like me, Big George was in no condition to risk crashing having been off the bike for three years due to two separate hip replacements but he was keen to start riding, his bike all set and ready to go, although understandably he was apprehensive and unsure how he would find being back in the saddle himself. From the start I was of the opinion the mountain, albeit for different reasons, would be good for Big George, something in front of him to climb; his need to reach Mont Ventoux was equal to mine.

The weather was unkind to us for the rest of October. Frosts were the order of the day. My rehabilitation continued well in the gym, as always, I was chomping at the bit to get out on the bike.

October 31st was quite a significant date, not only as it was the first ride for Big George, it was also the date when, in my opinion, the journey to Mont Ventoux really began from a cycling point of view. It was a dull, grey, overcast morning with a stiff icy breeze, bitterly cold, the temperature hovering just above freezing - but dry. That was good enough for me and Big George. Wrapped up against the cold we set off, steady as she goes, pedaling along familiar country lanes we had ridden countless times before. We chatted about days gone by, the many rides, adventures we had been on, it was nice to reminisce old times, also so good to be out riding together again after so long.

I could tell just by looking at Big George that he was struggling; there was no power to his riding no fluidity in his pedal action, he looked awkward and way out of condition, a shadow of the Big George I had cycled thousands of miles with in the past. I felt a sense of sadness deep down inside; I didn't like to see my friend like this. He wasn't complaining though and was glad to be out pedaling again despite the bitter cold. As I was looking at Big George, it suddenly dawned on me in fact I was looking at myself too. I too had no power, I was awkward, struggling to push a decent gear, I was badly out of condition despite all the work in the rehabilitation gym, I had no bike fitness at all if I am honest. The realization at just how unfit and out of condition we were at this point hit me hard, compounded as we climbed the short but sharp rise up past the donkey sanctuary. Slumped in the saddles on the granny gears as we call them - for the non-cyclists, this is the smaller chain-ring on the front crank, far easier gears usually only used on long steep climbs or mountains. We were spinning ridiculously easy gears and suffering badly doing it.

The low point, voices from behind, 'morning lads, cold one today' - I just about managed to acknowledge them as did Big George. The two elderly gentlemen that passed us going up the climb and it absolutely broke me psychologically. I could see in Big George's face that he felt the same way.

We didn't talk much on the few miles back to base, where we sat in the conservatory drinking hot tea, munching biscuits, generally dissecting the ride. To sum up, we were both very down and disheartened. Big George even questioned if he would ride again; he was ready to throw in the towel. It hurt me to see him like this although, in truth, I wasn't much better, if at all. I could feel the cracks appearing in my own resolve: maybe it had been too much too soon, maybe the Mont Ventoux was out of reach, an impossible goal perhaps? We had never been this out of condition or unfit on the bike. It felt like starting again. We hit rock bottom that day, it was a defining low point for Big George and me.

Looking back, it was a day we both needed, a reality check, a sharp reminder that it's perfectly fine to set yourself challenges and high expectations and to a point dreams, but there is a huge amount of work, dedication, effort and sacrifice to put in to stand any chance of realizing those goals and dreams. It broke us down that day but gave us the platform on which to build. It was now clear the size of the task and how much was required of us. We sat talking, trying to encourage each other as best we could, then, over a second brew, we looked at each other and burst out laughing. We laughed until the tears ran down our faces. In that moment we committed to the challenge through our laughter. Somehow, we would be ok; we hadn't got a clue how, but we just knew it would be ok.

7

Spiders web & Christmas cheer

My training routine was now set: Mondays, Wednesdays and Fridays in the rehab gym three hours at a time on the program; Tuesdays and Thursdays I was out on the bike with Big George; the weekends were a couple of rest days, for now at least. Each ride we would go a few miles further than the ride before. The weather was not kind, every ride bitterly cold, wet and windy. We wrapped up and kept on going out, encouraging each other. I drive down to Big George's house with the bike on the rack, get changed in the warmth of the conservatory, debating the weather as the rain played its merry tune on the glass roof above our heads. There were many days during that winter when I didn't really fancy going out, but Big George pushed us and we would ride. Likewise, there were days when it was down to me to kick us out into the freezing, rain and wind. We kept each other going. By then we were clocking up thirty to forty milers every ride and the pedaling was becoming more fluid, more natural again. Power and pace were way down still but I knew with mileage and hours in the saddle going back in the tank, the power and pace would improve in time. For now, it was all about the Big George formula: time and distance in the saddle. As I have said, a café stop has always been traditional on any ride for Big George and me and, as we were now clocking forty milers regularly, the café stops were back on the menu so to speak. Between us we can probably list just about every café within a seventy-mile radius of home. With this in mind, our next café stop was quite strange yet one of the best, and by pure chance.

Whilst enjoying our now customary post-ride tea and biscuits at Big George's HQ after a Thursday ride out, cold and a little wet, but happy with our efforts, we decided we would put a third ride in that week; we were both up for increasing the training, so it was agreed. Sunday morning, another dark, wet, windy, cold November scene. We set off with the intention of doing our first fifty miler, a nice loop out across open rolling countryside towards RAF Cosford, where there is a great museum I must add. A couple of cafés that we had used many times were within a short distance. Despite the foul weather the cycling was good and so were our spirits. Progress was definitely being made, short work was made of the thirty-plus miles that took us past RAF Cosford down to the railway café – which, disappointingly, was closed. No problem we thought, a quarter mile up the road was a good truck-stop café we had used for years, proper greasy spoon but a great place. Rolling up to the gate, to our horror this café was not only closed but completely gone. In the three years since our last ride over this way, one of our favorite stops had been replaced by a large caravan and motor-home dealership. I was gutted and the colourful choice of words coming from Big George, suggested he was not impressed either.

Things happen for a reason; I am a great believer in this. Rolling off with the intention of heading home, deflated in the knowledge that our café stop was off for today's ride, we noticed a small sign pointing to café. It led to a small roughly surfaced road running adjacent to the RAF base's perimeter. Sure enough, after a few hundred metres we arrived at the Spider's Web Café. Big George and I looked at each other in welcome confusion, years we had cycled over this way but never knew of the existence of what we now refer to as the 'Web'. The Web had been there for over seventy years, family-run, handed down over generations, the food proper good old-fashioned homecooked, hot and plenty of it, always busy, a lovely buzz and atmosphere greeted us, hot tea and sandwich to die for. What a hidden treasure.

I couldn't believe how we had never found this place before, but, boy, was I glad we had found it now. It was loaded with cyclists on a Sunday morning, which we loved; it was like coming home.

The Web was now our stop on every ride. No matter where we rode, we would end up at the Web, knowing there was only ten miles to return home. It became the norm to ride hard, getting in all the training miles before the Web stop. Then we could enjoy our cuppa and sani, using the ten miles back to base as a stretch and warm down; it worked well for us. We would look forward to and relish our Web stops. One foul and bitterly cold Saturday morning, we made a huge mistake, a schoolboy error in our plans. We had gone out early; it was barely light, the temperature hovering around freezing and strong winds pushed the freezing rain and sleet against the small areas of exposed skin on my face like needles; conditions were horrendous. We pushed hard mile after mile, taking turns riding at the front in the futile effort to give each other a rest from the full force of the weather. The last few miles before we reached the Web, we teased each other about how good the hot steaming cups of tea and toasted sandwiches to thaw us out from deep inside our bellies were going to be. So much so that by the time we rolled up to the Web frozen to the bone, I was salivating. We had pushed so very hard that morning; I had emptied the tank. Big George was in a similar condition; it had been hard miles. 'Oh no! oh no!' was the best I could muster

The Web was closed. How on earth had I not noticed before that it closes on Saturdays? We had been going there every Tuesday, Thursday and Sunday for weeks, but never on Saturday. It was my own fault; there in black and white plain as day, I had just never noticed. I was devastated, I could have sat down on the floor in the rain and cried; I was so cold and hungry. Clearly Big George felt the same by the dejected and beaten look on his face. Cycling, hard cycling will do that to you; it puts you firmly in the hurt locker sometimes. It was a long, miserable ten miles back to Big George HQ from there that day. A harsh reminder that planning is key on a ride. Cycling is the mother of cruel sometimes.

All was not lost; on our return Big George stepped in and saved the day. After we had changed into dry clothes, he knocked up a splendid bacon-and-tomato sani, plus as much steaming hot tea as we could drink, top man. It was a little slice of heaven. Munching and slurping our way through breakfast, we laughed and joked as always. We talked about the training so far and how we felt physically at that point - it was now the end of November. Happy with progress made so far, generally feeling we were doing ok, we agreed on the need to step things up a bit. Three rides a week of a good fifty miles a time was now the normal but more would be a bonus as we pushed on through the winter months. Clearly Christmas time would have a bearing on things and this was accepted. We both felt it would be beneficial to have some interim goals set between now and the Mont Ventoux the following June.

We had been including a few hills in recent weeks but nothing to strenuous. Our focus had been on building base miles, generally getting conditioned to being out on the bike for long periods (time and distance). Big George had read an article in a cycling magazine about a climb ranked at thirty-eight in

Britain's top one-hundred climbs, that lay not too far away from us. Twenty miles away, albeit deep into hilly Shropshire and Iron Bridge Gorge, stands Jiggers Bank. Plotting a nice route on the map that would take us out and round Shropshire, incorporating the climb, winding our way round to the Web for what would presumably be a much-needed café-stop, then home, all in about sixty-five miles. It all looked good on paper; we were up for it. It was decided the first week of the new year, just five weeks away, we would tackle Jiggers Bank. It would be a good test of our bike fitness, also without doubt a real acid test of our climbing legs too. The target was set.

With Jiggers Bank set as a target for early new year, the motivation to keep going out riding hard through the bitterly cold, icy, wet, windy month of December was made a lot easier. Big George and I were clocking some good miles and beginning to ride at a reasonable pace again; progress was good. My three sessions a week at Acton Heart provided me with a good base-level of fitness, also helping with my core strength a great deal, providing a nice balance to pounding the roads hour after hour. My physio and I continued to work on, how shall I say, keeping little Joe Chimp quiet inside me and I was finding it easier to keep control of the desire to go mad and red-zone it every now and then. It wasn't easy but I was getting there, psychology plays a huge part. I found it all fascinating learning and I enjoyed it.

We rode well through December despite the endless foul weather right up to Christmas. With a good couple of months riding and some hard miles now under our belts, Big George and I were feeling more confident about taking on Mont Ventoux.

A couple of days before Christmas I spoke to my bro-in-law Paul about coming out on a ride. As he was now on holiday from work, he was up for it.

'We will have to go steady; I've not been pedaling much yet,' he said.

This translated into a fourteen-mile-a-day commute on hilly terrain. I smiled; this was not the first time I had heard this from Paul over the years. I first met my now bro-in-law at the track way back in 1984. It was late April/early May, I had gone along with a friend of mine who was well established at the club. There was a full race program all weekend, and I was keen to watch as I was now into cycling of any kind. Already at the age of thirteen, if I wasn't reading cycling, watching cycling, talking cycling I was out on my bike pedaling; I practically lived on a bike at that age. Without hesitation when the invite to go along and watch a full weekend's racing came, I was in. I picked out a seat high on the terraces midway down the back straight, a great unspoiled view of the whole track and pits area. Instantly I was hooked. The racing was frantic, fast, at times dangerous, the crashes were spectacular, or at least from a spectator's point of view - I would find out later, not so spectacular as a rider. I was intrigued by the strange-looking bikes with no gears apart from the one they were set up in. The bit I loved the most - no brakes. I remember thinking 'these guys are crazy'. Flat out, full-gas speed, rubbing shoulders, digging each other with elbows fighting for position – and no brakes. Leaning on each other in the turns, no quarter given, no fear, I loved it. This really was the fast and furious, not for the faint hearted; I was so impressed. I was going to enjoy the weekend racing for sure. The junior and youth events were great, some fantastic racing. I couldn't wait for the seniors to start. This was my first encounter with Paul; the seniors started with both teams being announced to the crowd, followed by a few warm-up laps. The average age was approximately twenty up to, say, early thirties; then there was Paul, at sixteen not much older than me, scruffy mop of curly hair and small apart from his clearly visible monster thighs and calf muscles. It turned out these were not just for show either. The first time I saw him race it was clear just how gifted he was, and still is to this day, on a bike. He may have been a small scruffy looking kid, giving away years to his opponents but this counted for nothing. From first pedal stroke to last he was untouchable. Lightning fast, so much power, great bike-handling skills, the speed he carried through the turns was incredible. He was just head and shoulders above everybody and believe me there were some exceptional riders at the club; it was a pleasure to watch.

'Yes, mate, I have seen your idea of a steady ride before.' We both laughed.

We had arranged to ride on the Sunday before Christmas. I took the pleasant drive over to Alveley a small village in hilly Shropshire, and unloaded the bike from the rack. Two cups of steaming hot tea were waiting for us on the kitchen surface and home-made flap-jack. The usual micky-taking filled the air as we slurped and munched our welcome pre-ride snacks. Bitterly cold, windy and wet outside, Paul was keen to check out the Web. A route was planned that would take in a Web stop roughly halfway, covering a few hills and roughly fifty miles. Kitted up, we were ready for the off in good spirits.

Leaving the warmth of the house, the bitter cold ripped through us, heading off down the lane, the driving rain stinging our faces, leaning into the wind to stay upright. A curious cow poked her head through the hedge to take a look at us. I imagine she was thinking, 'you two must be mad riding in this weather.' I admit I was inclined to agree. Crossing the main road at the end of the lane, dropping down a few hundred metres, sharp right which was now bordering on icy, we hit the climb from the old mill to the top of the ridge, a climb of about a mile-and-a-quarter, average percentage gradient between six and eight. It made me work hard, legs burning by half distance, but I was maintaining a good cadence, (leg speed, revolutions per min, for the non-cyclists). Breathing hard, I could feel the benefit of all the hard miles Big George and I had put in over the previous months. I stood out of the saddle to push on.

Feeling comfortable, I looked across at Paul. Big daft grin on his face, as always taking the mick out of me, all in a good way. Me working hard, Paul sat there pushing some huge gears with consummate ease, making it look easy. He could have pedaled away from me any time he wished; I would have had no answer; this has always been the case. Years ago, we had trained together on the track and road for more hours than I can remember and even at my peak fitness and strength, Paul was too strong for me. On a good day I maybe pushed him a little bit at times but that's all. I feel fortunate to have cycled most of my life with exceptionally strong cyclists, better than me, but as a result it bought the best out in my cycling ability, making me a far better cyclist. Certainly, in my track days, I believe I achieved far more than I would have if I hadn't been constantly chasing the back wheel of Paul and others like him. We carried on cycling together long after our track days were over, in fact for most of our lives - good times, happy days.

We rolled along at a good pace considering the head wind. It was hard going. Laughing and joking as we pedaled on through waterlogged lanes and countryside that had a harsh, battered winter look and feel about it. Paul had clearly been pushing himself on his daily commute. He was pedaling well; ok he wasn't fit by his own standards but even as he was, Paul was stronger than most. As usual I was riding at my limit to live with him. It was just good to be out riding, sharing the road together again. Eventually we arrived at the Web, cold, wet, happy. Hot mugs of tea, and teacakes smothered in home-made jam, hit the spot. Feeling shot having pedaled hard to get there, Paul ribbed me blind he had me on the ropes as normal and knew it. We decided on a sneaky Kit Kat before heading back.

It's not often you get a helping hand from the wind but when you do it's a moment to treasure. Twenty miles out from home we turned and the wind was now directly behind us, raining hard almost sleet. Paul came around to take his turn on the front. Snarling at me as he came past, 'come on let's get the hammer down get back out of this weather.'

I didn't need convincing: 'let's do it'.

The next twenty miles were relentless, riding hard down on the drops right on my limits just to hold Paul's wheel. He would flick an elbow to call me round. I struggled to make the front and died a thousand deaths to hold the pace once I was there. Pushing on turn after turn, sharing the work and weather, flying along, full-gas. It was hard yakka but I loved it, feeling alive, buzzing on the adrenaline. Hurtling back down the climb to the old mill sat on the top tube, tucked in behind the bars, break-neck speeds, it was such a rush, my sternum screaming at me, but I didn't care. Hard on the brakes, scrubbing off some speed before the sharp left-hander, loose the brakes, throw the bike and your faith in the 23c tires, low into the turn, trusting them not to slide and let go in the wet conditions which would have meant certain disaster. We were through. Rolling gently up the lane with big silly grins on our faces, buzzing, just like we did all those years ago when we first started out. I guess we are still big kids at heart, especially when out on the bikes.

It's not such a bad thing in my opinion. It was a great ride. Chapeaux.

Christmas arrived we had fetched our tree. I have always loved a real tree at Christmas time it's my favorite part, our local farm shop always provides us with a great tree. Wrestled into the house, we always have a ridiculously large tree. The intense scrutiny began to find the tree's best side to face out into the room.

The lights, of which there are many, were loaded on. This is my job and I love it, once they are on that is; the pressure and stress of getting it right, good lord give me a bike race any day, it's far easier. With the lights all in place, everyone gave their seal of approval and my work was done. I sat and watched as the rest of the family set about decorating the bows with baubles and glass ornaments, little one-offs we had collected over the years. The miles of tinsel, the robin who always sits pride of place towards the front, glass snowman on top, the family-favorite Christmas grinch tucked away near the trunk somewhere. It was a special moment for me to be honest. This year it meant more than ever before. I sat and smiled, listening to the joviality and Christmas cheer, watching my daughters and crazy grandchildren constructing our splendid Christmas tree. I gave a private thanks in my mind to all the wonderful people who had worked so hard and performed a miracle saving my life, giving me the chance to enjoy this special moment and others like it. I am fortunate; it's times such as this I really appreciate the second chance I have been given. My advice, make the most of your special occasions, don't take them for granted; you never know what is waiting for you. The tree was finished at last; it was a real cracker that year. Feeling happy, over the next few days I gathered all the ingredients and turkey, I was looking forward to cooking the Christmas dinner.

Traditionally I had cooked on Christmas day for years but this year was special; I guess I was now just appreciating things so much more.

Christmas eve is midnight mass for us, the church decorated, a huge tree, the whole place lit up with candles, it's lovely. It must be said, I am not the greatest of singers, but we all love a good sing-along to the carols. It's a nice service, everyone happy, wishing each other well and good health. A cold, fresh, crisp walk home, then everyone settled off to bed. I was still sleeping as best I could downstairs in the chair due to the relentless pain in the sternum that would not allow me to lay down. That night, none of that mattered to me.

Sat with just the light of the magical lights of the Christmas tree for company, I reflected on the six months that had passed since my heart blip, and how different this Christmas would have been for my family if I had not made it and pulled through. I was glad for them as well as myself. I thought of the dark days where I was lay in the icu in a world of pain, right on my limits, struggling to hang on, the conversations I had with Mr Matuszewski, the kindness and care of the nurses, friends who had visited me and wished me well. Smiling at how weak and pathetic I had been on first starting at the Action Heart gym, the first rides back on the bike, I felt quite proud at how far I had come in six months. It had been a long, I admit at times hard, journey but I was still here and progressing, getting stronger every day. The rides Big George and I had done, he had worked so hard doing so well to ride again, I was proud of his efforts. He had helped me no end. For sure, there were days when he made the difference and I will always be grateful for his never-ending support. We still had a long way to go but confidence was building that we would make it. Mont Ventoux was waiting for us in little over five and a half months. Its mighty, imposing shadow was ever-present in my mind. For now, I just smiled and reflected on this whirlwind of events of the last six months.

That Christmas of 2013 was one of the best ever. We had a great time, everyone happy, I loved every minute of it, the memories will live on in me. As New Year' Eve came around, a strange feeling came over me: I had expected to feel like, 'thank goodness for that, get rid of 2013' but I didn't. Bizarre as it was, 9th June and my heart blip quite easily could have been my last day and in truth it was probably my worst, and, yes, there were many hard, dark days that followed, but events of that day also gave me things that I would never have experienced without the heart blip. I had found a lot out about myself, made new friends, learnt knew skills, gained knowledge about many things I wouldn't have otherwise. I looked at things differently now, in many ways for the better. I had experienced the true depths of my strength and resolve.

I appreciated life more than I had before and looked at the world and people around me in a very different way and I was grateful for this knowledge and understanding. With this in mind I said goodbye to 2013 - I was looking forward to 2014 and specifically to 9th June, when, as long as God spared me, the Giant of Provence, the mighty Mont Ventoux, would be waiting for me. There were still many questions to be asked of me and would I have the answers - time would tell. I had an overwhelming feeling that I now had a date with destiny.

8

Jiggers Bank

The winter sun low in the sky but bright, very little wind, clear blue skies, temperature around three degrees. The roads were mainly dry with the odd damp patch here and there in the shadows; conditions were just about as good as it gets for a ride in the wintertime. I was like a kid in a sweet shop, loading the bike on the rack; I was up for the ride, the fire burning bright inside, filled with anticipation. Driving my daughter Kelly to university we talked of the day's planned assault on Jiggers Bank, and of the trip to the south of France in June to take on Mont Ventoux. She was keen to have a crack at it, so it was decided she would come along on the trip too. The team was now complete so to speak. I was touched that she was so interested in coming along; it meant a lot to me. Dropping her at university I made the short drive down to Big George with a smile on my face and a warm feeling inside; it had been a good start to the day.

I was greeted as always by Molly, Big George's Irish terrier. She has bags of affection and a character to match. Surely there can be nothing more welcoming than the one shown by a good dog, just my opinion of course. Big George was in good spirits and well up for Jiggers Bank. I could tell by the look in his eye that he was fired up; it's good to see him that way. A few minutes later, Stig, Digger and Dave, another good friend and a strong cyclist when he puts his mind to it, arrived. The usual micky-taking, and joviality followed as we set off, rolling gently down the hill through the village, turning left then sharp right out into open countryside. Rolling fields, hedge-lined lanes, almost perfect weather for cycling. What a fantastic feeling, I appreciate days in the saddle such as this so much now; simple pleasures often mean the most. The twenty miles or so that lead our group over to Iron Bridge Gorge on the mighty River Severn was a lovely roll out. Undulating countryside that plays a game of deception with us cyclists – you're working a lot harder than you might think to ride at a seemingly nice steady club-standard kind of pace. All good training of course, picturesque villages with the occasional chocolate-box thatch cottage, beautiful old sandstone English churches every few miles, countless farms. That wonderful smell of the country in the air that you can only fully appreciate whilst out cycling or indeed walking, as I also like to do when not cycling. Those wonderful winding lanes eventually brought us out a Sutton Maddock island. A few hundred metres of main roads then sharp left back on to the lanes leading up to the top of the ridge overlooking the Severn Valley. A few miles away to our right lay Iron Bridge Gorge itself, the decent down to river below was roughly four hundred metres, on a road not much wider than, say, a farm tractor. Twists and turns, a nasty hard right on the steep twenty-three-percent section, its shallow point still hitting somewhere between six and eight percent. It's not for the faint-hearted. Resisting the natural temptation to brake too much, we made the treacherous decent down to a road that runs adjacent to the mighty River Severn below. It's maybe two and a half miles approximately, following the river along huge tree lines, buildings, landmarks all steeped in the history of this place as you would expect, given that Iron Bridge was the birthplace of the cast-iron industry during the industrial revolution. The Iron Bridge itself is a great engineering achievement. Along with all the museums, cafés, bistros and an abundance of crafts and local produce on show, it makes this a place truly worth a visit. For years I have cycled to Iron Bridge and sat a while having a break, on occasion treating myself to a hand-made pork pie from the family-run shop that sits right opposite the bridge. They have been making those pork pies, well, forever I think. I am no expert by any means but surely those pies have to be some of the best you will find. Believe me, for a hungry cyclist, and I am always hungry, they are perfect.

Having rolled through town, down past the Iron Bridge along the river, we made a right turn at the mini island just at the end of town. According to my research, this island is regarded as the starting point of the Jiggers Bank climb at river level. The elevation starts instantly at roughly three or four percent, climbing steadily for a good few hundred metres, passing houses and the village school. A wall of trees reaches high for the skies out in front, the road cutting away to the right, it's a dead give-away the land rising steeply away from you. Feeling the gradient increasing as we swung left up towards the village of Coalbrookdale, my thighs telling me things were beginning to get steeper with every pedal stroke. The long steady drags up through the village was work enough to reduce our constant banter to the odd word here and there, as we focused on trying to control our breathing. I could tell we were climbing but felt comfortable doing it; looking round at the boys, they were comfortable enough to. I couldn't help but think, 'this isn't so bad'; I was expecting much worse.

I was made to eat those thoughts in a big way.

Through the lights at a pinch point in the road we hit what is known in cycling as a 'false flat', (a drop-in elevation on a climb, giving a false feeling of riding on a flat road, despite still climbing) before the inevitable ramp up again. It was a welcome but short rest for our hardworking, now tiring legs.

Roughly halfway up the 2.4 km climb, passing under the old rail bridge, my eyes adjusting from shade to bright sunlight, I began to realize why Jiggers Bank was included in the upper half of Britain's top one-hundred climbs. The wall of tarmac in front of me rose up high and steep, far off, way up ahead in the distance, was a left hander which, even from that distance, I could see ramped up steeper still. Now the test would begin - my legs, heart and lungs agreed.

Now in full climbing mode, strung out up the climb in single file. Dave rode at the head of the line strong as an ox, mashing his big gears, closely followed by Digger in his relentless machine-like style; Digger settles into his rhythm and just sits there, grinding it out, exceptional. Stig, Big George and I lumped together, all trying to get our rhythm set in order to sit and tap it out all the way to the top. There was no denying now the climb was working us hard. Despite all the gains we had made in fitness and all the good hard miles pedaled, this was the first real, hard climb we had taken on and it showed. Definitely a whole new level, we kind of laughed, as Stig joked that we were now all, and I quote, 'fat, old and past it'. To be fair, at that point in time he wasn't far away from the truth. However, we would all work very hard in our efforts to rectify this in the coming months.

My research told me that as we reached the left hander, the percentage gradient would ramp up again to ten percent and over. Increasing further still between twelve and fifteen percent as the road swings right, maintaining the torture for five hundred metres to the summit. My research proved to be more or less correct. I was in the hurt locker now, desperately trying to arrange that almost impossible marriage between three people or in this case, cadence, breathing and gears. We all have this sweet spot, but I just couldn't seem to nail it down. The gears and cadence I would normally push on a climb like this, I simply couldn't breathe to cope with. Unable to get enough air fast enough to supply the demand for oxygen my body required to get me up the steep gradient, I was all out of sync and couldn't figure out why. Those last few hundred metres pulled my guts out and by the time I reached the summit my thighs had blown, my lungs were on the handlebars, and as for my heart, well, let's just say I don't think Mr Matuszewski would be impressed with the strain I had put his handywork through. Big George and I exchanged a look that said a mutual 'well done, mate'. A silent touch of gloves, we had ticked off the Jiggers Bank target that we had set way back in early November.

We pedaled on, happily chatting about the climb and the fact we were all now looking forward to a cuppa and sani some twenty miles of rolling hills further on at the Web. I was pleased we had all made it up Jiggers Bank, it was quite a stern test given the training up to then. With five months still to train for Mont Ventoux, I was pleased but under no illusion about the enormous amount of hard work still to be done. To put this into perspective, Jiggers Bank is approximately 2.4km long, an elevation gain of 400ft.; Mont Ventoux by comparison is 21.4km long, elevation gain 6270ft., clearly a world away from where we were on that day. Having said that, I felt day by day it was becoming a more realistic, less crazy idea, admittedly tough - but more realistic. It was a great ride by all the boys, a real pleasure to be out. We sat in the Web drinking our tea as though it was champagne on the podium. It was a memorable day out on the bike and good to ride together and, with or without targets, I appreciated every pedal stroke. Above all else I was just glad to be out.

Through the rest of January, Big George and I continued our three rides a week and our regime of two fifty-milers including some hills and a seventy-five miler on top. We had set ourselves a new target following Jiggers Bank: of riding a hundred-miler before the end of February. Out on a big loop including Jiggers Bank and the market town of Shrewsbury, we had something to aim for and keep us training. To be honest by now motivation was becoming less of an issue, our mindset and willingness to suffer on the bike were all good. Bizarre as it sounds, we were enjoying it; you learn to love the pain.

My rehabilitation program at Action Heart was going well - three sessions a week providing great cross training benefits, my general overall fitness, conditioning improving all the time. I was feeling quite strong again and core stability had improved massively since the heart surgery now some seven months previous. The one remaining stand-out problem was, as always, the sternum. The discomfort and pain were still way up on the scale. During my gym sessions the rowing machine destroyed me, every stroke like a hot poker placed against my chest. I was convinced my chest would tear itself apart, which was psychologically very unsettling and quite scary to say the least. It was and still is something I find difficult to handle - somedays its easier than others.

Paul and I had continued to ride on weekends. He was looking more like his old self, clearly pushing himself hard on the daily commute, strong and showing good pace. He would lead us out from Alveley over the River Severn into hilly country, breaking my legs up one big climb after another. He would keep me right on my limits the whole way. I am no match for Paul but these hard climbs he put me through week after week bought me on so much. We talked about the problem I was having pushing the gears and maintaining the cadence I had always done pre-heart blip; it had become clear that for some reason I could no longer push the same way.

We altered and played around with my gear ratios and cadence over a few weeks until eventually we found a set up where my breathing could supply my heart and lungs with the oxygen they demanded at the required rate. It took a while, but we got there, comfortably pushing bigger gears at a slower cadence and able to control my breathing while rattling along at a good pace, pre-blip the complete opposite. I had completely changed the way I rode to meet the changes within my, now much-reconditioned and patched-up, heart. I didn't mind this; I was starting to fly again, feeling some real power coming back to my legs and body. I could leap out of the saddle, put some real power down again, it was so good to feel this way. Paul was getting the best out of both of us. He would rile me up, get me chasing hard, we had some great rides but then we always did from when we were kids to this day.

By mid-February, training was progressing well both on the bike and in the Action Heart gym, where I was now due for an exercise-tolerance test that I had taken initially six months earlier. The only difference now being the test would be carried out in the Action Heart gym with my physio and a member of the cardiology team.

As before, I was hooked up to blood pressure monitors and the ECG machine with the usual spider's web of electrodes, cables, sticky pads. Heart-rate chest-strap secured, clothed in running shoes and shorts, the required attire for the test, I was good to go. The room was nice and cool, the speed and gradient gradually increasing as the test went on. I could feel the gains made over the last six months: every aspect of my fitness was massively improved from an aerobic point of view. I felt great and, even with my basic knowledge, I could see from the figures on the screen as I ran along at twelve-percent incline and climbing, my whole respiratory system was functioning well. I was processing the oxygen from the air intake far more efficiently now; my supply could meet the demand, the point at which I was required to stop passed. I was working hard, very hard, but the miles on the bike and hours in the gym meant my body was now strong enough to push on. My left leg no longer hurt and, apart from the visible scars, it felt as it did pre-blip. The only pain was in the sternum.

My limit was reached eventually, when I had passed the previous markers by some considerable distance. All the hard work had paid dividends, the staff and I were pleased, a very positive test result, I was on cloud nine. Following the shower, stopping off at the coffee shop within the hospital, I figured I deserved a treat a large latte and peace of chocolate cake, how good was that? I laughed as the naughty-but-very-nice cake set my taste buds jingling. As I say, I don't live like a monk; I do treat myself occasionally. When I do it's appreciated so much more these days. Simple pleasures, little things mean the most now.

My birthday arrived. That year was a strange one even for me. I say this as I have never found birthdays, mine to be specific, particularly easy for various reasons, but that's a whole other story. Waking I instantly felt different about the day; I don't know how best to explain it but at forty-two, when eight months earlier I was not expected to survive the night, checking out at forty-one, had quite an impact on me. I guess all that mattered: I was here and chalked off another birthday. I tend to now regard 9th June as my birthday, my second-chance birthday.

I celebrate this day far more than my actual birthday; it just feels right to me. It appeals to my odd sense of humor to celebrate the anniversary of the heart-blip as a birthday each passing year, as opposed to the date, technically speaking I almost should have died. It just works for me if that makes sense.

I hadn't made any plans as such for the day, although as a family we would do the whole cake thing later that evening with the grandchildren. Like me they do love a good piece of cake.

'Let's go out on the bikes, have a steady ride to the Web for poached egg on toast, Dad.' This was the suggestion from my daughter Kelly who happened to be on a day off and who am I to argue with a plan like that, I ask you? Changed into cycling kit, bikes loaded on the rack, we made the short drive to the edge of the sprawling countryside and parked up. Setting off, the morning bright, sunny, a bit windy but very mild for February, in short, a lovely morning to be out on the bike. At this stage Kelly was, in cycling terms, a novice, her fitness way above average as she lived in the gym and ran a lot. However, and I am not talking with my dad head on here but as someone who has seen and rode with a lot of good cyclists over the years, she can pedal well, has a good natural style, pedals efficiently in perfect circles as oppose to squares which most people do and handles the bike well. For someone so small and lightweight, she pushes big gears comfortably at a good pace. I often tell her if she took up cycling seriously the potential is certainly there to go places with it but she is just happy to ride out with her 'Pops' as I am known now and again. She enjoys it and so do I, both just happy to have the luxury of being able to spend some time together.

Rolling along, chatting, laughing, joking, stopping for various arty-type photographs along the way as that's Kelly's thing, the conversation got around to making the trip down to the south of France and Provence. Kelly asked what Mont Ventoux was like, how hard would it be to climb and did she have enough time to train for it.

I assured her that her aerobic capacity and general fitness were already at such a level she would be able to climb the Ventoux; it was more a case of clocking some miles in the saddle to become conditioned and comfortable being on the bike, to get used to handling it, to find and perfect a climbing style, and do some descending because coming off mountains at high speed on bikes does require some good bike-handling skills to get down safely in one piece. I was confident she would be fine and take it all in her stride. There was no pressure on her to ride the Ventoux; it was her decision to make right up to the day itself. For my own part I was just happy she was coming along on the trip with me.

There is just something right about poached egg and mushrooms on toast, a birthday meal fit for a king. We sat in the Web a while chatting, both looking forward to France, full bellies and happy. We had a lovely ride that day, as birthdays go it was pretty damn good.

The now customary debrief of the day's ride took place at Big George HQ over a cuppa and biscuits; it's the perfect start and finish to any ride as it sits right on the edge of the countryside, therefore eliminating any town-traffic riding just to get going or indeed to finish, usually at the point of exhaustion. Now, almost the end of February, a Sunday morning over a hot cup of tea, it was decided that early in the week would be the planned attempt on our first one-hundred miler. In truth we had been working hard since Jiggers Bank towards this target, our confidence was high that we would not just make it but ride it well.

The morning was bitterly cold, yet bright, sunny, a moderately stiff breeze, as Big George and I rolled away from HQ. I had the feeling of going on an adventure and was quite excited about the miles that lay ahead. I had reached a point where I thoroughly enjoyed my time on the bike again, almost as if I had time-travelled back to my youth, each ride filled with an enthusiasm, that freedom which being out on the bikes give:, no limits to your travels, each ride a new adventure. The majority of my best childhood memories stem from cycling. Cycling's been good to me.

The usual joviality ensued, rolling along winding lanes through the beautiful countryside that had become a second home these last eight months. After an hour, descending to the River Severn, following its course through to Iron Bridge Gorge, hard right at the end of town and our second climb up Jiggers Bank was underway. Now, don't get me wrong, no matter what level you ride at or what level your fitness is at, a climb like Jiggers Bank will work you hard. Most cyclists tend to ride at or close to their limits anyway, hence the old saying, 'it never gets easier you just ride quicker'. I would suggest this is roughly true; however, as your fitness and conditioning improve, so do your powers of recovery. If you combine this with good management of energy during efforts, you can feel your progress. All that said, as we hit the steeper sections towards the summit, Big George and I were in good shape. The progress we had made over the last six weeks since our first climb of Jiggers Bank was clear. Grinning at each other like daft schoolboys, it was a big psychological boost.

With our tails up, we pushed on hard now, riding high on the confidence boost. We had to cover thirty-five miles from there on our chosen route, taking us into Shrewsbury. We hammered it. Big George was in good form; he had lost a lot of weight by now, his big legs grown considerably in mass and strength. Those roads were ideal for him; he was putting the hammer down and me firmly in the hurt locker doing it. I didn't mind, we took turns on the front, riding hard all the way into our planned café stop at Shrewsbury. It was a pleasure to see Big George riding so well again; it made me smile inside.

There is a coffee house in Shrewsbury within view of the train station where they serve a wide variety of teas always in a proper pot, freshly brewed coffee, made well, any way you want it. A choice of freshly made sandwiches and pastry's which, it has to be said, are very good and healthy to. Local artwork hangs on the walls, live music plays on occasion; there's nice rustic feel about the place. I love that a lycra-clad cyclist is welcome and can sit next to a high-flying suited-and-booted business type or a college student and everything in between in comfort. It's a lovely atmosphere, the staff are super-friendly and genuinely nice people. This café became a regular stop for Big George and me and I must thank the staff there for taking good care of us. They always washed our bottles out and refilled them with fresh water for our ride home, much appreciated.

Freshly brewed coffee and a pan chocolate, two actually, I was ravenous.

I looked at Big George. 'Mate, I'm shot.'

Now that I had stopped and sat down, the cost to my energy levels from the hard ride in was clear. I was cooked and the flushed look on Big George's face told me he wasn't feeling much better either. If this was Big George HQ, not a problem but by even shortest route back we were thirty-five miles out, so not so good. Another coffee with some sugar added bought a little more rest but was only prolonging the long slog home. It wasn't mentioned but we knew the one-hundred miler was now off; the ride became a war of attrition to get home without bonking. 'Right come on then, lets crack on.' Good old Big George.

Lumps of wood replaced my thigh muscles, or it felt that way. The coffee and pan chocolate had picked me up, giving a much-needed boost, but despite this I was running not much above empty. There is no easy ride back from Shrewsbury; whichever route you take there is a huge ridge in the general lay of the land and, like it or not, we had to climb over it. Hitting the climb just through the village of Cressage, the climb winds up from three miles out, gradually ramping up to twelve percent over the last half mile. The lower slopes put us to the sword and, as we hit the twelve percent section up to the summit, we had blown up. It was horrible, painful in fact, I don't know how we made it up there. I had emptied the tank. Now pedaling squares, we crested the summit and rolled a few hundred metres down the other side. Pulling over for a breather, pushing flapjack and water down our necks, it was all damage-limitation now, just get back, we were dangerously close to bonking and hitting the red.

Fifteen miles further on, stopping again, we laughed, taking the mick out of each other for committing the basic schoolboy error of going out too hard and burning way too much energy too soon. This error had left us in the energy-depleted state we were in now. Desperate times call for desperate measures - all the food and water we had left we shared, which measured out at two mouthfuls of flap-jack and three mouthfuls of water each. Just under ten miles to go to the safe haven of Big George HQ and the endless supply of water, tea and biscuits we would graze on, on our arrival. Those last few miles were pure torture; every little piece of me hurt and tunnel vision set in. I found it immensely difficult to control the bike at all. I could barely turn the ridiculously light gear; I had been forced to push or pull the brakes. After what seemed like an eternity we made it. Bikes dumped unceremoniously against the garden wall, we slumped in the chairs, absolutely shot, no question we had completely emptied the tank.

As I sat looking up through the glass conservatory roof, watching the clouds race past in the blue sky above, I smiled to myself. We had failed in our attempt to clock our first hundred-miler of this comeback adventure, by just five miles as it turned out. It didn't matter; sure it was disappointing, but we proved that day our strength and fitness was good. In truth, probably at a better level than I had thought. What I took from that ride most: from a long way out we were cooked, we suffered like dogs and kept going, having to dig deep, right down into the pit of our resolve and we kept going. I was proud of myself and Big George that day; it was our own fault we ended up in such a state, but we had that dig-in, won't-quit, ability to suffer and keep going back in our legs and psychology now. I recall thinking if we were to suffer on the Mont Ventoux as I believed we would, we could still keep going. Failure on that day would not be an option.

It had been a monster ride. Big George and I often look back on it as a defining moment, a definite line in the sand; we started to truly believe in what we were doing all this for. With three months hard training to go, we felt good. The whole adventure was gathering real momentum.

Meeting the man with the hammer.

February gave way to march. Generally the weather was now getting warmer which made the persistent wind and rain more bearable during many long hours spent out on the bike. By now I was riding four or five times a week and Big George came along on at least three of these. Stig and Digger were clocking up some good mileage and doing a couple of spin classes a week, which they were feeling the benefit of, and we all rode together when we could. Kelly rode with me on her days off, progressing well from a virtual novice to being able to hold her own on any club-standard ride in only a few short weeks. I was impressed by how quickly she had taken to cycling, most importantly she enjoyed it. Paul continued his commute and he and I would ride together in the hills on a weekend. We were all doing well, putting in the miles, fitness improving, feeling positive about making the trip and about climbing the Ventoux.

Paul and I had planned a ride for one Sunday morning. Big George was out of action due to a family gathering of some kind - he didn't miss many rides. I laughed as we headed out from Alveley into the driving rain and strong winds. I could imagine Big George sat in the warmth of his conservatory drinking a cuppa and laughing at our expense, knowing the battering Paul and I would take in conditions like this. I would be disappointed if he wasn't; I would do the same.

Alveley down to the River Severn at Arley is a long winding descent, beautiful and carefree, rattling along, crouched low over the bars at break-neck speeds, throwing the bike low in the turns, fields rocketing past in a blur, what a rush. At least it would be if this were a nice, hot, dry, sunny day in middle summer. That day, in driving rain and wind, it was horrid. The lanes were covered in mud washed off the fields; rivers of muddy water ran furiously downhill, covering the dangers of many pot holes. I was tense, gripping the bike a little tighter than I should have been and the back wheel began to slide from under me. In a split second my weight transferred to one side causing the inevitable to happen - bang! Down I went, meeting the cold, wet, muddy, hard tarmac, sliding across the road like Bambi on ice, down into the ditch. I may have filled the air with the odd hint of blue as I got up. Luckily no damage done to me or the bike, it was just a reminder that, if you cycle a lot, from time to time you will come off, simple as that. Provided a good laugh if nothing else.

Dismounting, we walked over the foot bridge at Arley, pausing a while to look down at the mighty River Severn below, in full flood, smashing her way downstream through the valley. So beautiful in summertime, frighteningly awesome in winter. The climb up out of the valley on either side is brutal, a real leg-breaker as any local cyclist will tell you. My opinion: the side we were now on, taking us up past the old steam railway station to the top of the ridge some distance beyond is the toughest, a couple of miles of painfully steep inclines between ten and twenty percent, false flats, one sharp kick up after the other. Paul as always made it look easy pushing his monster gears, me riding on my limits just to live with him, but I loved it. Cresting the top of the ridge, heading off through the back end of the Wyre forest towards Bewdley, Great chips to be enjoyed there if that's your fancy, looping around the town and out in to open country once more towards the little town of Cleobury Mortimer, some miles away over brutally leg-draining terrain.

The thing about cycling this side of the river, you're either climbing a short, as in anything from a few hundred metres to a mile of ridiculously steep climb or 'leg-breaker' as I like to call them, or you're hurtling down the other side at warp-factor ten, crouched over the bars, hanging on for dear life. There is very little in between. It's hard yakka as we say, hard miles, but great interval training; it really puts it in your legs. Paul's dad has always said 'if you can ride a good club-standard pace on these roads, you can ride anywhere.' I am inclined to agree with him, it's so hard - but great cycling.

A little under a mile outside Cleobury Mortimer, the road ramps up in terms of gradient, marking the start of a long hard slog for the next five or six miles that gives you no rest, culminating in a brutal climb over the last couple miles of between six and ten percent, up to the summit of Clee Hill itself. The views from the summit of the Clee are amazing. On a clear day you can see for miles all around, way off down into Wales with her many lumps and bumps standing tall and proud on the horizon. Today however there would be none of this on show; even from five miles away I could see the summit was shrouded in cloud and mist.

The headwind tried its best to push us back down the road as the climb up through the village with its famed crooked church spire gave way to the baron open-looking country on the lower slopes of the Clee. Hard yakka, taking turns on the front to share the wind, I was beginning to feel the effects of mile after mile of climbing all the leg-breakers that had bought us to this place. Our objective for the days ride had been to climb the Clee, loop round and head back. A short false flat of around two-hundred metres, then bang! - you hit the wall of tarmac that signals the final brutal couple of miles to the summit, steep, relentless in short - horrible.

Paul and I decide to put in our maximum effort up this section of the climb then have a short break. I quickly settled in to my newly found climbing rhythm, feeling strong, pedaling free and easy even on a climb like this. By this stage I was quite fit. Paul asked if I was ok.

'Yes, mate, you push on; I'll see you at the top.'

He grinned and leapt out of the saddle. I had no answer and he powered away from me as though I was stood still even though I was moving at a respectable pace myself. I sat tapping it out with a smile on my face, watching with pleasure as his slight frame, with those huge legs turning his monster gears, powered away up the steep road ahead. Paul was in his comfort zone, doing what he does best, climb. I have never yet ridden with anyone who can climb like Paul and, believe me, I have ridden with some very good climbers. He is exceptional in the hills. As a cyclist, it's a pleasure to see someone ride like this and to share the road with them.

In no time Paul was away and gone far up ahead. I was locked in my own battle with the steep slopes of the Clee. It's that pleasure and pain thing, every part of me hurt, working hard, pushing, right on my limits, yet, bizarre as it sounds, I love this feeling. I can have a good old growl at the world, vent some steam in this scenario and its ok, gives the inner chimp a chance to rattle his cage a little bit with no harm done.

Climbing well, pleased at how my strength and fitness were improving every ride, it was a good hard test of endurance with lots of climbing in foul weather at a very tough pace, as always trying to hold the wheel of and live with Paul. I was now massively improved from the frail, broken-down version of myself who had climbed back on the bike way back in the October the year before. Munching flapjack on the summit of the Clee in the wind and rain, I felt quite proud of myself and the way things were progressing.

Short work was made of the non-stop up-and-down route back to Bewdley, opting for the Trimpley reservoir side of town which would hit us hard with a ridiculously steep climb of a couple of miles, before a few miles of gentle descent back to Alveley to finish. Suddenly, we were daft teenagers again, just as we were all those years ago, hitting the Trimpley climb we were racing. Let me rephrase: I was racing, flat out, full-gas, maximum effort; Paul was playing with me like a cat with a mouse. Until the inevitable happened; my legs blew up and he powered away, leaving me for dead, laughing his head off. It's not cruel; I was laughing to. It's always been the same - happy days.

Gently rolling down the descent back into Alveley we laughed about rides and adventures in years gone by, winding our legs down nice and easy. Showers all round and that great post-ride feeling filled my body. It's like floating on air. A nice cooked meal was waiting for us and, in good spirits, we talked about the Mont Ventoux. We were looking forward to getting out there, to riding the slopes where so many of the greats of our sport had graced the slopes before us. Despite the days foul weather, we had put in a good ride, almost six thousand feet of climbing in a fifty-mile loop. Chapeaux to us I say. We deserved our dinner.

March was coming to an end, bar a few days we would be into April and time seemed to be passing with increasing momentum. It had been a month since Big George and I had failed in our attempt to clock our first hundred-miler. We decide to go at it again, with a good month's training now back in the tank, we set off from HQ. It was an overcast day but dry and very mild for the end of March, so much so in fact that it was a gift to be able to ride with one layer less than normal, all adding to the general feel-good factor of being able to move more freely on the bike, and just that little bit lighter to. There was a slight breeze but nothing to bother about; all was good in the world.

Familiar winding, undulating lanes through open countryside which now, dare I say it, had the look, feel, smell about them that suggested spring was almost there, not quite but almost, the signs were there and it was so good to see. The lanes led down to the main road, leading past the old Dudmaston Estate. It's a lovely place but the road here is too fast and carries too much hgv traffic for a cyclist to feel safe. I was grateful not to be on it for long. Peeling off right on to Church Lane or, as Big George and I like to call it, the 'Post Box Climb', due to the wonderful old fashioned post box standing proudly at the foot of it.

It's a very picturesque area as you climb up through the trees, but a horrid climb on a bike. From the off it breaks your legs, pulling your lungs out and today was no exception. I was now of the mindset that, no matter what climb was in front of me, I had no option but to climb it, because nothing I would face could possibly compare to the brutal unforgiving slopes of Mont Ventoux. Up we went, hard yakka indeed, grinding it out, talking each other up the climb. Big George and I function very well together on the bike. Despite our very different styles, we just fit somehow. I don't have to think about where he is or flick an elbow to call him round and his wheel is a safe and solid one to follow. I would hope he feels the same. The many hours and miles ridden together just make the whole thing easy. 'Well done, mate, another one climbed.'

Pushing on down to the old market town of Bridgnorth, over the mighty River Severn which was now far less flooded, which is always a good sign of approaching spring, then a short sharp climb up out of the town through tight streets of old black-and-white houses. It's a nice town.

Now I have never ridden the Paris-Roubaix (prestigious one-day classic pro road-race) and have nothing but the upmost respect and admiration for those that have. Greatest rider never to win this toughest of classics: Big George Hinchapie, just my opinion but we all have one right. The Morville road which we were now on, must be the worst surface I have ever had the misfortune to ride on bar none. It is one layer of broken, crumbling, poorly packed tarmac on top of another. It is not the cobbles of the Paris-Roubaix, but it might as well be; it shakes your teeth loose and jars your joints and bones to their very core. The bike vibrates underneath you like a jack hammer, chain flailing about like a whip. You feel as though the bike will fall apart and your spine shatter with every pedal stroke. It's a perfectly horrid few miles in every way.

Craven Arms bear left, the road sign rescues us from that awful surface. Swinging gratefully left, the surface was now silky smooth by comparison, a breath of fresh air, indeed it feels like you're riding on it until, sure enough, a few hilly miles later the novelty wears off. Cycling is so hard on the body in more ways than one. Craven Arms, our intended first café-stop en route was still a good few hilly miles away yet, through beautiful countryside where a well-earned coffee and slice of treacle tart was waiting as reward for our efforts so far. Well, it's rude not to; that's my excuse and I'm sticking to it.

Pushing on from Craven Arms toward Church Stretton is a main road carrying a lot of traffic although, to be fair, if you ride sensibly there is enough room. Generally, the hgvs and motorists treat you well, along this stretch at least. That road is made for Big George; his big legs come around and take the front and I watch the chain make its way down to the eleven-tooth sprocket on the rear cassette. He pushes that 53/11 gear like a diesel engine. He can motor along on roads like this but I'm soon on my limits. We're working hard, taking turns on the front, low on the drops, legs pumping to maintain our pace. We were flying along now; it was a great feeling to be riding so strong again and the grin on Big George face suggested he was feeling good, enjoying the ride. We were happy.

Past Church Stretton swing a left, it took us out and upwards to the Shropshire Hills, an area of outstanding natural beauty. My legs would have argued at this point, as the name would suggest it's very hilly, all climbing but lovely cycling nevertheless. Climbing well today, out of the saddle, free and easy in good bursts, tapping out a good rhythm and cadence when sat down. Pushing some big gears over those hills, it was clear we were now way stronger than a month previous. We hammered down the far side of a winding descent, a nice dry road for a change filled us with confidence, just letting the bikes roll full-gas, a well-earned treat for our efforts on the long climb up. Low sweeping right hander toward the village of Minsterley. Big George was on fire, really motoring; I was on the ragged edge just to hold his wheel. Keeping a strong pace towards Shrewsbury, mile after mile, we kept the hammer down all the way into town, sweeping round the river to our favorite café stop, the Shrewsbury Coffee House.

The window seat is our favorite spot; we can watch the world go by and keep an eye on the bikes locked just outside the window. The friendly staff greeted us with a smile as always and took our bottles to wash and refill and our order: two coffees, two toasted ham and cheese panini, and a piece of chocolate marble cake to die for. Lunch had never tasted so good. We had put in a strong ride of just over seventy-eight miles with a fair amount of climbing, all at a good average speed. The most pleasing point - how good we were feeling. Sure we could feel the ride in our legs, but we were not tired like a month ago. There was plenty of energy left to burn, helped further by the nutritional value of the lunch now being enjoyed so very much. Each time I cycle to Shrewsbury Coffee House, I promise myself that one day I will drive over there so I can sit a while longer and just relax, savoring the whole atmosphere of the place more. You cannot afford to stop for too long on any ride; it is tough to get going again if you stop to long. We thanked our friends in the café, it had been a lovely stop as always but now for the final leg home.

Fueled up and suitably rested, rolling out of Shrewsbury towards Atcham, gradually building the pace again. Soon we were hammering toward the village of Cressage, Big George setting a furious pace along the old Roman road. It was great to see him in such good form but, boy, did he make me suffer! The beast of a climb that had wiped us out a month earlier now rose high in front of us. Keeping the hammer down we launched into the climb at full gas. Settling into our climbing rhythm, we were working hard, yes, very hard, but a climb like this will always work you hard. We were fitter now and way stronger; all the time and distance in the saddle was paying dividends. This time there was no slowing down, no running out of gears, no bonk, no collapse, we climbed strong and felt good doing it.

Reaching the summit, a look of acknowledgment between us was enough said. Back down the Paris-Roubaix Morville road into Bridgnorth, over the river it was all a blur, motoring on along the lanes we had labored so many hours month after month through the winter. Today there would be no warm-down over the last ten miles; Big George was on a mission. It would be full-gas all the way into HQ. I was up for it anyway, such a great feeling those last few miles. I knew we had broken through the hundred-mile barrier by now and to be able to ride so strongly with so many hilly miles behind us was a massive boost to our growing confidence in our ability, endurance and, most importantly, belief in ourselves.

The cuppa and biscuits went down a treat. We were riding high on our achievement, a much-stronger-than-anticipated ride of just over 116 miles in total, a landmark ride, our first century since getting back on the bikes. It had been a cracker, happy boys indeed.

April arrived in typical fashion, lots of sunshine, lots of showers, also the temperatures were a lot warmer, and I don't mind the odd light shower out on a ride, it helps keep you cool. The training was going well, everyone clocking up some good miles. Kelly now up to riding fifty- to seventy-milers comfortably at a good pace, climbing well too. Everyone was in good shape with just a little over two months before we faced the Giant of Provence on 9th June, hopefully in the sunshine.

Paul had been on the phone; he was off work for a week and the plan was that I would pick him up. We would all meet Big George at HQ and do a Shrewsbury ride from there. It was a beautiful morning, clear blue skies and sunshine plus the rare treat of almost no wind. I recall thinking this would be a quick day and I wasn't wrong. Both Big George and Paul have a healthy competitive edge as I do myself, so, as you can imagine, following the immortal words, 'we'll have a steady one today', from the off it was basically full-gas. Between Paul and his exceptional climbing power, and Big George with his awesome time-trailing ability, I was in for a hard day.

The countryside was definitely in spring mode. The air had that wonderful earthy smell about it and had taken on a cool fresh feel. I have always appreciated being out in the countryside but post heart-blip, I appreciated it so much more even at the furious pace being set by Big George and Paul.

In no time we made the river crossing at Bridgnorth, up and out of the town on to the Paris-Roubaix Morville road stretch, powering on towards Much Wenlock, swinging left on the long climb across Wenlock Edge, heading for Church Stretton. Lovely cycling country, rolling fields, lots of hills. It was hard yakka especially riding with this pair, who were edging each other on with each passing mile but we were rewarded for our efforts with breathtaking views and the pleasure of being out there.

It was constant climbing all the way to Church Stretton, the pace insane. We pedaled well and Paul left Big George and me in disbelief at a ridiculously steep section near Brockton, where the road rises up for a few hundred metres at over twenty percent; he just grinned and big-ringed away from us like we were stood still. We had no answer other than to nod our heads in respect of his ability on a climb. Eventually we made the climb up and over Hope Bowdler, making the long and very fast descent down to Church Stretton itself. Swinging right at the lights, now back in Big George terrain, roughly a fifteen-mile run into Shrewsbury from there on gently undulating road, Big George hit the front hard his big pistons of legs smashing out his 53/11 gear with consummate ease and I focused on his back wheel, my front almost touching to squeeze every bit of drag I could just to hold on. Paul tucked in tight on me, we rotated round taking our turns on the front then dropping back and so on. I was riding on my limit the whole way and between them they had me in the hurt locker all day long. I didn't mind this at all however, as an average Joe, always cycling with cyclists who were way better than average, it bought the best out in me. I have had to develop the ability to dig in, suffer, endure, block out the pain and keep going when my body and mind are screaming at me to stop. I am grateful for this; without it I would never have made it through those dark days in the hospital when I really just wanted to quit. That mentality, born on the bike, kicked in and I just kept going. Some have suggested to me that years of pushing myself on the bike contributed to my heart blip; well maybe, maybe not, I like to think cycling gave me the physical and mental strength to survive it. You be the judge.

As we sat laughing and joking enjoying our perfectly brewed fresh coffee and warm pan chocolate in The Shrewsbury Coffee House, I smiled to myself. It was good to feel so comfortable and relaxed after the effort put in over the last sixty hilly miles that we had covered to get there at such a brutal pace. Forced to ride on my limit the whole way, I recovered quickly, a clear indication that my fitness, strength and overall conditioning was now at a good level. I could see it in Paul and Big George too. It was a big confidence boost to feel this way. It had taken a while, but everything was coming together nicely. Psychologically, I was in a good place.

Our bottles and bellies now full, rolling out of Shrewsbury heading for Atcham Bridge, swinging right on the old Roman road and away, heading for Buildwas and Iron Bridge Gorge beyond on a wonderful warm sunny afternoon. It was the first time I had ridden in just shorts and a shirt for a long time and it was great to feel uncluttered and free of the layers forced upon me by the winter, now thankfully behind us. The pace just as furious as on the outward leg of the ride, by the time we followed the River Severn into the Gorge I could feel the hard miles of the ride in my legs. Climbing out of town, up the horribly steep climb from river level to the top of the ridge, Paul put in a burst, leaving Big George and me for dead; we were riding a strong pace ourselves but couldn't match him. We laughed at how easy he made it look, but it was anything but. Over the ridge and down, it was only about twelve miles back to HQ from there. It was full-gas all the way in. On reflection, that ride has to be one of the quickest I have done since my track days back in the eighties I thoroughly enjoyed it; I know the boys did too. It was a strong ride. I knew we weren't far away from where we needed to be.

It was a beautiful spring morning, sunshine and clear blue skies, I was due to attend my Action Heart program but had the flexibility at this stage to attend any time during the day. It was the last day of April, odd for no reason it stuck in my mind. It was still early six-thirty am so I wolfed down a bowl of porridge, banana and honey, grabbed the bike headed out. There was still a chill in the early-morning air, but it was always shorts and shirt now - you soon warm up.

By the time I reached the end of my street, my route plan was set: I would head to Bridgnorth, cross the river heading out the back of town on the Broseley road eventually dropping down into Iron Bridge, all basically undulating road with a good few climbs along the way. Once in Iron Bridge I would climb Jiggers Bank then head back along the same route in reverse, no stops just out and back, a nice sharp fifty miles. I hadn't ridden on my own in quite a while and it took a little getting used to. The scenery was amazing as always; I will never tire of looking over hedgerows at our wonderful countryside. We are fortunate indeed to have England's green fields so close to hand.

I am not sure why, maybe it's just me, but when I ride alone, I tend to push myself a lot harder or at least that's how it feels. I never really understood why I feel like this, given I am usually killing myself to hang on to the wheel of, or take a turn in front of, whoever I am riding with. Maybe it's just a psychological thing but the fact remains that, whenever I ride alone, I always empty the tank. Today was no exception. As my great childhood inspiration Laurent Fignon once said, 'sometimes when we train, we simply have to go out to meet the man with the hammer'. I kind of get what he meant. I was really getting into cycling in a big way during the early eighties when Laurent Fignon was in his heyday. For me as a kid, he was a larger-than-life character and I was inspired by his relentless power and ability to suffer on the bike. My dad bought me a replica of the team system u shirt for which Fignon raced at the time; I was about fourteen at the time. I still have the shirt today and, unbelievably, it still fits and I do ride in it on occasion for old times' sake. I have to thank the great Laurent Fignon for the inspiration that lead me to cycling properly and a lifetime spent riding bikes. Chapeaux professor, may the wind be forever at your back.

I reached Jiggers Bank and put the hammer firmly down; whatever my best was at this point, I was going to unleash it now. I pushed down hard on the pedals pulling up on the backstroke with equal force, finding my rhythm quickly, focusing about twenty metres ahead. Climbing well, I could feel it all just flowing, perfectly in tune with the bike underneath me.

Hitting the steepest part of the climb, I jumped out of the saddle and danced on the pedals, feeling a definite surge forward. I had real power in my legs again; I had that kick. I felt strong, in control of my breathing, stamping on the pedals with authority. I was meeting the 'man with the hammer'. Jiggers Bank held no fear for me now, smashing my way up to the summit. I rounded the island at the top and began the descent, laughing out loud, crouched low in a tight tuck, sat on the top tube, hurtling down the descent flat out, I was grinning like the Cheshire cat. Four months earlier this climb had broken me, put me deep in the red in a world of pain, left me doubting myself and weather my goal of Mont Ventoux was achievable at all. That day I had powered my way up the slopes of Jiggers Bank a different person: stronger, fitter both physically and psychologically. I had danced my way up the climb without a care in the world. That is the pleasure side of the whole pleasure-and-pain scenario that goes hand in hand with cycling. Occasionally you are rewarded with the pleasure that comes from long hours and hard miles in the saddle. That one ride now and again where all factors come together in your favor and you ride in that sweet spot; it's an amazing, uplifting feeling and you have to appreciate and savor every second of it, every pedal stroke and inch of the ride, as though drinking a fine wine in some sun-soaked vineyard in the deep south of France itself. Such days don't come often but when they do, boy, do I love it.

Cycling back the same route in reverse, I made short work of the climbs and rolling countryside. It was a pleasure to be out on such a beautiful spring day. On my return I showered and re-fueled on pasta and fish with some good fresh fruit and a couple pints of water. I sat and rested for a couple of hours before making my way over to the Action Heat gym and on my arrival I felt fully recovered. That was a measure of how far my fitness and general aerobic health had progressed. My physio and I debated recovery and rest at some length during my session that afternoon. She was a smart cookie and I was learning a lot from her. This knowledge was having a big impact on my progress, no question about it. Her help was invaluable to me.

April gave way to May and there was just a month of training to ready ourselves for the Mont Ventoux. Happy and confident, we were all in a good place although, I admit, now it was so close I was getting a few butterflies in the tummy, I had been expecting this to be honest. I couldn't wait; I would read endlessly about the Ventoux; it was now my soul focus, dominating my thoughts. Still more miles to ride, more hills to climb, more hard work to be done, but the wait was almost over.

10

Happy valley & Bara Brith

May arrived with her warm sunny days and ever lighter evenings, the miles became easier to pedal somehow, all the horrid long hours and miles in bitter cold wind, icy rain, through the winter months were now a distant memory. My cycling stripes as I like to call them had started to appear. Cyclists have the strangest-looking tan lines and I am quite proud of mine to be honest: middle thigh to just above the ankle, middle bicep to the bottom of the wrist. Cyclists look like bronze gods but looks can be deceiving; the rest of our bodies are milky white and have the build and complexion of a plucked chicken pre-oven, I kid you not. It's without doubt a freakish look but all part of cycling. I was relishing the luxury of being able to ride in a cycling jersey and bib shorts every ride now and, if you ride and train all year round, such balmy days are very well-earned, believe me. Light-weight shower-jacket is rolled up tight, tucked away under the saddle just in case, but these were the lovely days of May. Indeed, life was good.

Big George had a lovely static caravan just outside Tywyn, situated on the Cardigan Bay coast, southern side of Gwynedd in beautiful Wales. It is a lovely part of the world down there from a cyclist point of view. If you want to ride in beautiful scenery whether it be coastal roads, winding country lanes, rugged open countryside or, my personal favorite, the hills and mountains, then go there, you really do have it all. No matter what your choice of machine - road or mountain bike - give Wales a go, you won't be disappointed. These parts are also home to the wonderful Bara Brith, roughly translated 'Welsh Tea Loaf', but in my opinion it's far more than that. I could happily eat Bara Brith until I explode, I love it. Also, the humble Welsh cake, although I won't enter into the furious debate as to the traditional recipe for these wonderful treats. All I will say is that, whilst in Wales, I have never had a bad one, fantastic bike fuel. Stick a couple of these bad boys in your cycling jersey pocket, they will keep you fueled up for miles trust me. So much nicer than any vile energy gel you could use; no thanks, I choose the Welsh Cakes every time and then some.

Big George had invited me to join him in Tywyn for a few days. He had to take care of a few things down there and he saw it as an opportunity for us to use the time as kind of a pre-Mont Ventoux training camp in the Welsh mountains. A test for our climbing legs out on some good, long, hard climbs, before tapering the rides down a little towards the end of the month ready for Mont Ventoux itself. For me, it was a no brainer, 'perfect mate count me in'. We looked forward to the trip the following week; it felt like a reward in many ways for all the hard miles and hard yakka that Big George and I had put in over the last seven months or so. I felt like a kid in a sweet shop.

Greeted by another beautiful, warm, sunny May morning, I left the house, threw my kit bag in the motor, loaded the bike on the rack and set off on the short drive to pick up Big George who was ready and waiting with his big grin as always. Bags in, his beloved trek (road bike), gleaming and immaculate as always despite the tens of thousands of miles it's covered, loaded on, away we went at last, laughing and joking like a couple of silly school boys on a trip, happy days indeed.

It's quite a strange feeling to drive along familiar lanes where normally I would be cycling, doesn't feel right somehow. Over the magnificent River Severn now in a more sedate summer-looking flow, up and out of Bridgnorth onto the Paris-Roubaix Morville road, I could still feel the awful tarmac surface despite my motor being a 4x4 pick truck, cleverly adapted by Paul. As well as an exceptional cyclist he is also a very gifted engineer. Thanks to his skill set my truck was able to carry eight bikes safely and with ease. Swing left towards Craven Arms, Big George commented on how far we had become used to riding on a regular basis thinking nothing of it. Seventy- and eighty-mile rides were now normal for us. It had taken some hard yakka to reach this level again but we were comfortable doing these distances, and at a respectable pace too.

Sailing through Craven Arms, passing one of the many café stops we would normally use on a Shrewsbury ride, we headed for Newtown. It was a lovely day for a drive; we discussed Mont Ventoux and how we felt about it and what we imagined it would be like. By then, between us I think we had read everything that's ever been written about the Giant of Provence. We were confident we had done enough training to reach our goal but we were under no illusion as to how tough a ride it would be. Passing the hours talking of cycling adventures we had enjoyed so much in years gone by, we found ourselves driving along the sun-soaked estuary between Aberystwyth and Tywyn on the edge of Snowdonia National Park, such a beautiful place. Bare right along the coast road, I love the ocean, that day wind-swept, white-crested, deep-blue, choppy waters, powerful and rugged looking, a breathtaking coastline for sure. Through Tywyn along the coast a couple of miles tucked away in the hillside is the site where Big George's caravan sits. Picture perfect views of the coast and mountains, just the noise of the breeze and the birds, and the pure air makes you feel alive. Bikes were soon unloaded, and kit stowed away, sitting outside in the early evening sunshine with a cuppa and, of course, cake, there was a rare moment of silence. Big George and I sat there just soaking it all in; we didn't need to say anything, a grin and a nod of the head said it all. We had earned these few days and the fantastic cycling that was to come.

Up early the next morning, despite the slight disappointment at a dull, overcast but dry dawn, we remained upbeat and eager to get out on the bikes. Big George did us proud with some lovely fresh locally-bought mushrooms and poached eggs on toast, washed down with several cups of strong hot tea. Changed and kitted up, pockets stuffed with goodies to keep us fueled out on the bikes, we headed out. It was a little chilly being so early but not unpleasant, rolling down the hill, stretching my back and ham strings as I did so; the peace and quiet were overwhelming, the perfect dawn chorus. Rugged coastline on one shoulder, mist-covered mountains on the other, a mixed but wonderful serenade of birds and gulls above as we rolled along gently turning the legs, warming up into the ride. Pure clean air filling my fully expanding lungs, I felt privileged to be in this place, feeling so strong. Money cannot buy these times or feelings. That morning I was the best I had been since the heart-blip, one of those moments that has stuck with me and I will never forget.

Rolling through Tywyn a short way, looping round stunning country lanes in a quest to find a climb known locally as Happy Valley. It's a beast of a climb of a good few miles. Sharp left at the foot of the climb, the gradient instantly ramps up to around six percent remaining constant at this as you wind your way round the beautiful valley and up through the tree line. A few miles out from the summit, the gradient ramps up again ten, fourteen, twenty percent, proper leg-breaking stuff. Big George and I were strong by now, working very hard but comfortable with it. The last two-hundred metres are just ridiculous:

twenty-three up to twenty-eight percent, hurt-locker time for any cyclist. But up we climbed, stopping at the summit for a breather and some photos of the stunning scenery all around from our wonderful viewpoint. Pleased with the way we had climbed up Happy Valley I was puzzled that this climb didn't make it into Britain's top one-hundred climbs alongside Jiggers Bank. I don't know the criteria but for what it's worth: in my opinion Happy Valley is way tougher, not that it really matters I guess, I enjoy both.

Pictures taken, we hurtled down the descent enjoying the view and taking great care to avoid the odd stray sheep wondering around in the road. I figure they have the right of way, after all it's their countryside and we are their guests in it. Looping round back towards Tywyn briefly, swing a right picking up the old road to Dolgoch Falls, amazing scenery all around, I always appreciate days out on the bike but to pedal in this kind of country made that day's cycling a little bit more special. Big George was in good form, lean again now he had built his legs back up to what they had been prior to his double-hip-replacement surgery. He makes light of it to be honest, that's his way, but to have both hips replaced and come back as strong as he now was, was quite a remarkable achievement. I have the deepest respect and admiration for his efforts. I had seen with my own eyes just how hard it had been for him to get back. He was now the Big George of old, powering along with consummate ease, it was a pleasure to see and share the road with him. Chapeaux sir.

Stopping to take more photos at Lake Tal-y-llyn, it started to rain quite heavily so on with the shower coats. It didn't spoil the days ride at all. Sometimes I find it very peaceful riding in the rain; it has a strange calming effect on me somehow. Climbing rugged terrain that wound its way through awe inspiring country, no rush or urgency, yes, we were training still but today we just rode for the pleasure of it, albeit at a good pace as our level of fitness was now in good shape. The long, and in places brutally steep, unforgiving climb to the highest passable point by road of Cadair Idris, is (I believe but I could be wrong) second only in height to Snowdon itself in Wales. Regardless, the climb was a doozey, working us hard, but we rode strong getting our rewards at the top. As we sat taking a drink and a well-earned snack, the rain stopped and within minutes the sky cleared and glorious sunshine burst through the crystal blue, revealing the true beauty and splendor of the landscape and mountains we had been blessed to climb.

Thankfully, the now quickly drying roads made the high-speed descent from Cadair Idris a little less of a white-knuckle ride. Tight hair pin bends, steep drops, a very technical descent but the scenery is worth it. Picking up the Dolgellau road, Big George came steaming round to take the front. Full gas now, he put me on the ropes, hammering it for the next half an hour or so, working together to scrub off the miles on the busy road section - we tend to avoid main roads where possible; it's far safer to use the B roads and lanes of which there are more than enough if you take the time to use a map. Waving goodbye to the main road, pausing a while to appreciate the view while crossing the old wooden toll-bridge at Pen-y-Bryn, taking the opportunity to pack away the shower jackets as the sun was now baking, it was indeed a glorious day.

Hungry, is a word very familiar to any cyclist. The number of calories you burn per hour is vast. I seem to spend my life in a semi-permanent state of hunger. We decided to have a nice café-stop in sunny Barmouth a few miles up the road, Big George and I were indeed more than ready for some food on arrival. Bikes locked up, we took an outside table at a delightful sea-front café. I smiled as the warmth of the sun warmed my bones. Freshly brewed coffee arrived along with home-baked, right there in the café, Bara Brith. Oh, my lord does it get any better than that? The rich spiced-tea flavor and the sweetness of the fruit, bang! Just hits the mark. I savored every mouthful. That and the big scoop of vanilla ice cream I had with it. What? I was by the sea; it's the law.

Several cups of coffee later we made our way out of town and over the impressive wooden bridge spanning the estuary at Barmouth, pausing a while, midway across, to take some photos. The blue sea and golden sands gave way to the mountains we had labored up and over earlier, a truly stunning view as far as the eye could see. We rode on into the afternoon sunshine following the coast around Cardigan bay, up and down its many undulations, hard yakka but I hardly noticed, I was enjoying the day and the ride so much.

I really did feel as though the culmination of all the hours, miles, of hard work came together that day. I felt fitter, stronger, happier in my own skin than I had in a long time. The miles clicked by, pedaling free and easy, by late afternoon we had arrived back at the camp. It had been a great ride, one of my best days in the saddle ever. For me personally, after the ride that day, I knew in my own mind I was ready for Mont Ventoux. Confidence was soaring, physically I was strong, psychologically I was focused and ready to go. Big George was more than ready too. I had seen his whole demeanor become relaxed over the course of the day's ride; I could see it in the way he was riding, strong, powerful, but easy and comfortable with it. We had come a long way together, the fruits of our labor over many months were plain to see. It was a great few days, riding again the next day. We even rode up Happy Valley twice- just because we could, we climbed for fun. The pressure had gone from our rides now. I enjoyed those few days cycling round Wales with Big George so much, they did me the world of good and I will always be grateful to him for taking me. Big George's wife Lynn came up to us a couple days after our arrival and we all went to a fish restaurant in Aberystwyth to enjoy a wonderful meal and a glass of wine. We sat talking late into the night, feeling happy and relaxed; the whole trip had been the best possible medicine.

Generally, the rides for May were shorter, tapering down to forty or fifty miles a ride, also easing up on the intensity. It was nice cycling, enjoyable in such nice sunny, warm, weather. Big George and I made the odd ride into Shrewsbury just to stretch out our legs a bit, but nice and easy. Digger and Stig had been clocking some good miles and, by combining this with spin classes, they were reaping the benefits of their efforts. Kelly had also continued to progress and perform well on our rides together. Coupled with her constant gym work and running, I was in no doubt she was more than fit enough and capable on the bike to ride Mont Ventoux without a problem - if she decided to ride it on the day. Paul was riding more miles and we continued to enjoy our hilly rides together on weekends. We were all in good shape for Ventoux.

Training in the Action Heart gym three times a week gave me perfect cross-training off the bike and my core strength and general conditioning were in good shape; being continuously monitored was such a confidence builder. I knew my stats were good, blood pressure always spot on, resting pulse super-low again, I felt great. The only negative, the constant nagging pain in the sternum, always present, no escape from it, in some ways this constant reminder of events helped to keep me in check; it certainly helped in the daily battle with the inner chimp. Little Joe was still constantly trying to take over my new, more controlled and measured approach to training in the gym and indeed to cycling. Some days I admit the chimp would win, getting the better of me; I would go bananas and push way harder than I should, but overall I was being good. This was in no small part thanks to the hard work and patience of my long-suffering physiologist and now good friend. Hours spent talking and debating psychology in sport, making changes to my approach whilst training in the gym had made a massive difference.

The old me pre-heart-blip would have simply self-destructed and burned out, probably even done some serious damage to my heart or worse; looking back, I can see that now. It's not an excuse but pre-heart blip I was a cycling product of the early eighties, well before the days of structured science in sport training-methods. I had grown up in cycle racing when coaches rode you into the ground and, if you weren't suffering in a world of pain, on your ragged edge, you weren't working hard enough or trying, I would come off the track on training nights exhausted and almost at the point of collapse. I was of the mindset I had to kill myself every track session and training ride. Of course, with the knowledge we have today, it's clear these methods are not the best, far from it. For me the psychology of completely changing my training methods was as bigger an ask as getting back to physical fitness ever was. I learned so much and enjoyed it in truth. I am a different kind of cyclist now and I think a better one for it. Sure, I am too old to compete but I am much happier now in myself and in the way I ride, more than I ever was racing as a hot-headed youngster.

I won't say I look back on the track days with regret, I enjoyed those years and achieved a lot, but I can't help wonder sometimes: if I had the approach then that I do now, how much further I could have taken it? None of that matters now, I was reborn as a cyclist or this is how it feels to me at least; I am ok and comfortable with it. As the saying goes: you live and learn. I was happy to learn and more than happy to live.

Continuing to clock miles through May was easy given the weather, which was glorious every day, a pleasure to be out there and Big George and I made the most of it. Towards the end of the month we managed to find a day where everyone was free, a rare treat but a timely one as this would be the last ride before making the trip down to the south of France to climb Mont Ventoux.

Everyone gathered at Big George HQ. It was a bright warm sunny morning and spirits were high, clearly all concerned were looking forward to the trip which was now just a little under two weeks away. That day's plan, a fifty-miler, a nice and steady undulating route including a stop at the Web which had become like a second home, a pre-Ventoux-trip bacon sani as a treat then a steady roll back to HQ. The whole ride was very pleasant and relaxed and I couldn't help but notice the massive difference in us all, a totally transformed group compared to the one that puffed, panted and died a thousand deaths, clawing our way up the slopes of Jiggers Bank way back in January. I was quite humbled that these friends of mine had all worked so hard to get themselves into the kind of shape required to climb a mountain like the Ventoux with me. I was immensely proud of them all and rode with a smile from ear to ear that day.

Bacon-and-egg sani had never tasted so good. We sat around the large table, discussing the upcoming trip down to Provence in the deep south of France, going over the final arrangements, answering any concerns, making sure we all knew what was happening and when. At last mixed in with the laughing, joking, truck load of micky taking, we arrived at the point where we were all singing from the same hymn sheet. Ahh and relax, like it was ever in doubt.

I couldn't have asked for a better pre-Ventoux ride, rolling along in the sunshine, enjoying the moment; the lanes I had spent so many long hours riding through the harsh and bitter cold, wet winter were now dry and warm, almost smiling at me, surrounded by green fields and crops well on their way to summer and the harvest beyond. Stig rolled alongside me, expressing his concerns that he felt his fitness might be a little down from where he would have liked, worried he might possibly slow us down on the climb up Ventoux and he didn't want to affect anyone's ride. His wish on the day would be for us all to carry on at our own pace and leave him to grind it out in his own time. It was an honest, heart-felt gesture on Stig's part. I could see he was genuinely concerned so I assured him no one would be left behind; we would all ride up together. I had been touched by his willingness to make the trip and ride the mountain with me in the first place; no way was I leaving him or anyone else behind, it's just not me.

The last few miles along the sun-soaked lanes, I couldn't help but think back to the darkest of days back in New Cross. Had it really been almost a year? There had been so many ups and downs since then. Physical and psychological battles almost daily. It hadn't been plain sailing to get to this point; I had suffered like a dog at times, having to grit my teeth and push on through the pain more times than I can count or wish to. I had doubted myself so many times; there had been days when I could have happily taken a hammer to the bike and quit never to ride the thing again, times in the Action Heart gym when I just wanted to stop, pull the monitors off and simply walk away, days when I hated the whole idea of the Mont Ventoux altogether. But for every bad day, there was a good one to build me back up again. I am the type of person that needs a goal, something to aim for to keep me going, that keeps me strong, motivated; I am your typical all-or-nothing type. Having the Mont Ventoux as a target had kept me going physically and psychologically. I was fortunate too in having good family and friends around me who supported me and gave me the space I needed to focus. My long-suffering but dedicated physiologist Ioanna had somehow managed to help me learn how to control my inner chimp, bringing that much-needed, measured approach to training without which I would have self-destructed for sure and certainly failed. The knowledge, help and support she gave me was invaluable.

Big George of course, what can I say about him? I had spent the vast majority of this epic journey training hard alongside him and there was no question I wouldn't have reached the level I was at now without him. He had pushed me, driven me on when I needed it most, rode with me when the weather was so bad we really shouldn't have gone out but he came with me regardless. Long hard miles in the saddle: time and distance are Big George's philosophy and we were living proof that this philosophy still works today and there is no substitute for it. We had come back from nothing to where we were then at, ready to take on what is regarded as one of, if not the toughest, climb in cycling. Rolling the last few metres into HQ, I looked across at Big George, held out my hand; he looked back with a grin and we shook hands. We didn't need to say anything, the look said it all; we had toiled together long and hard to get here and now we were ready. Next stop, the South of France, The Giant of Provence, the mighty Mont Ventoux.

11

The Road to Provence

With all the training now done, June arrived at last with sunshine and lots of heat. Boy, the days had got very hot very quickly and down in the south of France, it was baking. I was watching the weather down there like a hawk. The mistral winds were known to whip up without much, or indeed any, warning, battering the Ventoux with storms that would make it impossible to ride even with my stubborn attitude. I knew if I was unlucky and this happened on the 9th June it would mean postponing until the next day or the day after and so on until the weather broke enabling us to attempt the ride. I would be devastated if this were the case because, for me it was always about the 9th June, the first anniversary of my heart-blip. Right now, it was looking good, a week away the long-range forecast for the area was for hot, sunny, temperatures in the mid- to high-thirties. That would certainly do the trick; I was just hoping for a dry day with very little wind.

Paul and I had given my old motor a good checking over. She was a tired old girl with 250 thousand miles on the clock but reliable as time and tide; she was good to go. It would be a mammoth round trip of almost 2,000 miles there and back; I was looking forward to it but then I have always been cab-happy. All the necessary kit was packed in to meet European law on route, everything squared away nicely. Over the next couple of days, I collected all the luggage, bikes were dropped off at my house ready to load on the day of the 6th when our two-day journey would begin. The plan: to arrive in Pernes les

Fontain, a small medieval village a few miles outside of Bedoin the town at the foot of Mont Ventoux, on the evening of the 7th giving us a day's rest at our farmhouse location before taking on the Ventoux on the 9th. All was ticking along splendidly until I gave my bike a final once-over. I had cleaned, oiled, adjusted everything, fitted new tubes and tires, new chain, brake pads a few days before and she was in perfect order. For some reason I can't explain but I am glad I did, I gave her just one last check - the back wheel was not running free; it was making a horrid noise. I could feel it grating, grinding and snatching, the free wheel and bearings were shot, no time to mess about we were leaving the next day. Maybe this was an omen, I don't know but just as I was leaving to buy a new rear wheel Paul rang me with exactly the same problem. I couldn't believe it. What were the chances, I ask you? Paul was in a flap as he had to work up until the last minute

'Mate,' I said. 'I'll sort it out.'

Two hours, two new wheels, tubes, tires, cassettes all swapped over and the bikes were good to go. Never a dull moment.

Digger and Stig had been round to see me, dropping their bikes and luggage. They would be flying down to Avignon on the Saturday afternoon, meeting Big George, Paul, Kelly and myself at the farmhouse in Pernes les Fontain. All being well, we would arrive at around eight that evening after our two-day. epic road trip. Kelly and I checked and double-checked that everything was finally ready and all set to go. All that remained was a night's sleep, load the bikes, then on our way at last.

Friday arrived, motor loaded to the brim with bikes and luggage all secured. My family came to the house to wave Kelly and me off; it had been a long hard journey for them also, from the darkest of days a year ago, when they thought I wouldn't survive the night, to today, when I was about to leave to begin the journey to hopefully put the final piece of this epic twelve-month adventure in place. They had suffered with me, supported me in the many ups and downs along the way. There were a few tears and strained nerves as Kelly and I pulled away then, at last, we were rolling. I couldn't quite believe I was finally on the way. It had been a very long year for much of which the Ventoux had seemed a lifetime away. I had thought of little else but here I was, just a few days from facing this mammoth goal I had set myself all those months ago. I couldn't wait, I had stomachache already; I was fired up for the challenge. Bring it on.

Big George was ready and waiting, grinning from ear to ear; he was looking forward to the trip down. We were a little conscious of time, the dash to Alveley to pick up Paul who had to work until lunchtime, then high tail down to make our crossing over to France via the Channel tunnel. Almost two-hundred miles on a Friday afternoon, hmm interesting, shall we say. Eventually all on board and away, me at the wheel, Big George riding shotgun, Paul and Kelly tucked up in the back, making good time, all well in the world. It wasn't a bad journey to be fair, apart from a few hold ups around the infamous M25 section. Making the Tunnel Terminal with enough time to spare to grab a coffee, the pressure was off. A pleasant evening, I was feeling good, Kelly was a little nervous about the Tunnel, the idea of being under the sea didn't rest easy with her. As we drove onto the huge train and began to move, she was a little more comfortable with the idea, albeit opting for sitting in the motor the whole way until we emerged on the French side in Calais. I had been impressed by the tunnel, what a remarkable feat of engineering. It was easy to use and I would definitely take this option again in the future. Already in my head I was planning each year that followed: as long as I was able, I would return to France to ride another tour mountain on the 9th June.

For me personally, the most iconic three are the Mont Ventoux, Col du Tourmalet and Alpe d, Huez, but that was all to come. For now, the focus was the Ventoux. The short drive of a few miles from the tunnel to our overnight stay at a cheap and cheerful hotel in Calais was enough to round off a good first day. Checked in, the plan was to meet at seven for breakfast and be on the road for eight; we had a long way to go. Kelly was soon asleep. I was so glad to have her along; I lay in my cot with a smile on my face still unable to believe I was finally there in France. It was all becoming very real. Excited as though on Christmas Eve, tomorrow I would see with my own eyes not in a book or the tv screens but in reality, Mont Ventoux.

Fresh Croissants and coffee, sun streaming through the glass-fronted restaurant, views out over the crystal-blue sea, I could think of worse ways to start the day. Only seven am but the warmth of the sun was easily felt.

Breakfast enjoyed, we set off. Turning on the sat nav, we were somewhat taken aback: exactly 600 miles to reach our destination in Pernes les Fontain, definitely a road trip! The first few hours through northern France I was surprised how vast the country is, huge open spaces, lots of agriculture not unlike Britain in appearance; I was impressed. The joviality and banter died to a subdued almost silent hum as we passed through areas where some of the most horrific battles of World War One took place, huge expanses of rolling fields. It was eerie; the road cut through the centre, mile after mile of nothing, every now and then a white monument stood tall and proud for all those brave, poor souls who made the ultimate sacrifice on both sides. What I had gone through to get there suddenly faded into insignificance compared to the hell those brave souls had faced. Driving through in respectful silence, I was moved by the experience; I think the others were to, and rightly so.

Skirting Paris, by late morning we had made good time, scrubbing off a few hundred miles. We didn't see much of that famous old city except, as expected the Eifel Tower was easily visible, a box ticked. The true Romance, for me at least, still lay some four hundred miles further south.

The further south we drove, the more France began to look as I had imagined, cities became towns, towns became villages, boulangeries, patisseries, beautiful street side cafés, breath-taking countryside - and cyclists, lots of them. It was great to see, kids, young and old people on bikes of all shapes and sizes. I loved it.

Sunflowers I love and they were everywhere and the vineyards were so vast and the chateaux's that stand on them so grand and proud in all their splendor. Yes, southern France is definitely for me; everything about it was picture perfect. I had never been before but I felt like I had come home.

Early afternoon, we had a short break for coffee and pastries to die for. I couldn't help but chuckle to myself at just how good these freshly brewed and baked delights were. I could happily have sat drinking coffee, eating pastries until I burst. So good. A little under 250 miles to go, already Digger and Stig had arrived at the farmhouse and said how lovely it was. I was relieved they had made it and that our home for the week was going to be comfortable. I was looking forward to seeing them later.

Finally sat nav told us ninety-nine miles remaining, after five hundred miles it was a relief to see just a two-figure distance remaining. By now the scenery was breathtaking, a huge fast-flowing river had been company for quite some time and the land was lush and green, most exciting for me - it was starting to become hilly, very hilly in fact. Some good climbs were visible in all directions; what a playground for a cyclist. Seventy miles out from Pernes les Fontain, my heart-rate increased a little as the mountains came into view. I couldn't believe what my eyes could see, bearing in mind that at times in my life I had ridden the highest mountains that Britain has to offer, and, yes, the British 'mountains' are majestic and awe-inspiring but they are nothing compared to what lay in front of me now. The British ones are mere hills by comparison.

The mountains were huge, rising up out of already hilly terrain, reaching high into the clouds many with their summits above the cloud layer, some with snow clearly visible on the top. It was June and 35 degrees, how was that even possible? Dumbfounded at the sight, there were not just one or two, they were everywhere, as far as the eye could see, all around, way off to the horizon. My heart was now thumping hard with excitement; this was the real deal.

Mont Ventoux has a very unique profile, a long gradual slope on the one side climbing up to the summit, the other side a brutally steep elevation. Roughly speaking it's wedge-shaped, the reason being, it was a volcano that erupted and blew the one side clean off. That's my non-scientific cyclist's description but you get the general idea. However you see it, one thing is for sure: the Ventoux is instantly recognizable. However, with so many mountains touching the skies, I thought it will be difficult to spot until we get close. How wrong could I be? As always it seems - very.

Mile after mile, mountain after mountain we would say 'that's it' with equal enthusiasm to any of them; they just kept on getting bigger. Almost at the point of us giving up trying to spot it, laughing, taking the mick out of ourselves, we rounded a long sweeping left-hand bend in the road, following the river through the valley floor, sky-scraping mountains on either side and silence descended on us, on our guessing which of these mountains was the Ventoux.

In front of us, without any doubt or question, was the Giant of Provence. It was clear why she is called the 'mighty' Mont Ventoux, she stood way above everything else in view, she towered above all the other mountains. Sat nav confirmed that she was forty miles away and she was massive even from that distance. I looked and stared in disbelief. She was huge, imposing and scary in the extreme. The cloud layer only reached halfway up her slopes. Even from forty miles away, clearly visible were the three-or-so miles of hard, baron, white rock at the top toward the summit where nothing grows because the air is so thin. For a few minutes none of us spoke a word, as though we had entered a church and were being respectfully silent. Despite all the research, nothing could have prepared us for the reality of what was now towering in front of us. I had read a poll taken by professional cyclists as to which tour-climb they feared the most; I now understood why they voted overwhelmingly for Mont Ventoux.

Filled with anticipation, excitement and, I would be lying if I said without, a certain amount of apprehension, the last forty miles seemed to fly past. We talked of the massive ride that awaited us in a couple of days. Soon enough our thoughts turned to the beautiful and typically French town of Pernes les Fontain. It was as I had imagined: a mixture of medieval and rustic buildings, window shutters, Mediterranean-looking roof tiles, lovely shrubbed gardens and lavender everywhere. One thing to be said about the whole area: vineyards, lavender, sunflowers they were everywhere, beautiful place; I fell in love with it straight away. Our accommodation for the week was typical of it, large roomy three-story rustic farmhouse with its own swimming pool and beautiful gardens and plenty of space for us all to spread out. It would be perfect; I felt at home here. It was so hot, the pool was a huge bonus. Stig and Digger were waiting to greet us as we arrived, it was early evening. Gear stowed, rooms sorted, the six of us sat around the large table in the kitchen, raising a glass of wine to our health and the ride to come. We had made it; we were there at last, in the shadows of the mighty Ventoux.

I had opted to sleep downstairs in an armchair - I still wasn't able to lay flat with any degree of comfort a year on from the heart surgery. I had however mastered broken sleep in a chair to the point where I could survive on a few hours' rest a night. The sun was beating down on the large glass-covered sunroom at the back of the house and, at six am, it was already warm enough to walk outside in just a pair of shorts. The pool was so inviting, cold against my skin as I eased myself into the water although gone were the days I would have dived in without regard for my heart which would probably not stand such an entry now. Floating around, I could feel my whole body relax as the cool water and sun's rays worked their combined magic on my muscles. What a great way to start the day.

One by one the others appeared, reveling in the sunshine, making good use of the pool. Kelly and I made the short walk to the local patisserie in search of croissants and pan chocolate. It wasn't hard to find, the wonderful smells from the patisserie led the way.

Beautifully baked baguettes, loaves, croissants, pan chocolate, all to die for, you must hand it to the French, they certainly know how to bake. Me being me, I bought enough to feed a small army. I don't have the vocabulary to describe just how good those fresh, perfectly baked delights were but the silence that fell as we all tucked into our breakfast sat around the pool, with tea and coffee to wash it down, said it all. It was a little slice of heaven.

That first day was all about relaxing in order to get over the long journey and rest up ready for the next day's battle with the Ventoux, plus it was Sunday after all. After a leisurely morning, we took a gentle walk into town. Big George had offered to prepare a meal that evening and Big George is a wonderful cook; some of the best meals I have eaten came from his culinary skills. The local shops and market stalls were only open for a few hours during the morning but the produce was pure quality, all fresh and locally raised and grown, cheap by comparison to back home. Big George soon had us loaded with bags of beautiful salad, vegetables, chicken, cheeses, fresh breads and, of course, locally produced wine of which there are many in this area. It would be a pre-ride celebration feast fit for a king. I was impressed by the few streets of the medieval town we saw on the groceries-hunt. Plans were made to return that afternoon for a better look around, although only a little after ten am the temperature was 35 degrees and climbing rapidly, our fresh produce needed the sanctuary of the fridge and we all needed to cool off in the pool.

One thing remained a constant reminder of the reason I was there: no matter where you were, the huge imposing figure of the Mont Ventoux was visible, dominating the clear blue skyline. She stood looking down and, although roughly ten miles away, she was immense. I couldn't help stopping once in a while and staring up into the sky. There is an iconic weather station on the summit but from where we were it looked like a pin-head touching the edge of space. I couldn't quite get a grip on just how vast this Giant of Provence was.

After a few pleasant hours splashing in the pool and generally lazing around, Paul, Kelly and I decided to take a gentle stroll around Pernes les Fontain; Big George was staying put, resting and soaking up the sun; Digger and Stig were planning to wonder down later. The old medieval town was all I had imagined: rustic, typically French, cobbled streets, lavender, sunflowers, many other varieties of beautiful flowers adorning picture-frame windows and boxes. Kelly, in her element, took arty type photographs at will and we visited an art exhibition in one of the many churches. The town was full of character and history. The many cafés, bistros were a delight. We had bought hand-made ice cream and sat on the shaded steps of the old monastery, watching the river which circled the town meander its way along the high stone-built castle walls, and generally watched the world pass slowly and peacefully by.

Winding our way up the steep, cobbled pathway which lead to the viewing gallery of the impressive castle, which once stood guard to this wonderful town, the views across the valley below were a sight to behold. Rolling fields of green and gold, huge purple expanses of lavender, vineyards, mountains for a back-drop on all sides, and, of course, the Ventoux itself. Digger and Stig were already there when we reached the top, leaning on the wall looking up at Ventoux. I was in awe of it, the nervous tension growing deep in my stomach. I knew it would take every millimeter and second of the training I had done to reach the summit. In truth, nothing I had done to this point in my life as a cyclist could have really prepared me - how could it? I was confident, yes, but nervous also. Stig was showing a few signs too and Kelly wasn't saying it but I could see the doubts creeping into her mind. I felt she was more than capable but I didn't intend to push her; I was just happy she was there with me.

Top marks to the chef. Big George had prepared a wonderful meal: slow-baked chicken with garlic and various herbs, potatoes roasted the same way, one of the best salads I have ever eaten, fresh bread from the patisserie. So simple but you could taste the difference in the amazing produce from the local markets and, in true Big George fashion, there was plenty of it.

We sat around the huge rustic garden table to enjoy our meal, the warmth of the sun still on our shoulders, early evening yet the temperature still in the low twenties. The conversation was light-hearted, the tales of cycling adventures growing longer as the wine flowed. It was a lovely few hours spent together and a better pre-ride dinner we couldn't have had.

I had had the idea to have cycling jerseys made for us a few weeks before, not so much a team-kit, more a memento of the occasion and, in some small way, a thank-you for all the effort everyone had made to come down here with me on this crazy adventure. It had been a big ask, I know; I will always be grateful to them. Our meal now finished, I took the opportunity to hand out the shirts and they seemed to go down well. We raised a toast, 'a safe ride good luck, Mont Ventoux'. The chink of glasses, smiles all around, it was a nice moment.

Everything cleaned up and squared away, I decided to take the drive down to Bedoin, basically to recon the route we would cycle in the morning from Pernes les Fontain to the foot of the Ventoux in Bedoin. Just in case you're wondering, due to the medication I was on for my ticker, I wasn't drinking at all. The run down through town was easy enough, out towards Carpentras, picking up the signs for Bedoin, it was a straight road all the way through rolling fields of lavender, crops and vineyards. It would be a lovely few miles just to turn the legs.

The small town of Bedoin is beautiful and typically French. I recognized the sweeping bend out of town, that signifies the start of the climb up Ventoux, from years of watching Le Tour du France on tv and from the countless cycling books I had read over the years. I drove just a couple of miles up the lower slopes; the gradient was around 6% but it looked flat by comparison to what towered above, mile after mile of it. Pulling over in a layby of sorts, I got out to look up at the Ventoux, up close and personal at last. I admit she put a certain amount of fear into me but she lit my fire inside also; it was a surreal moment; I felt like a boxer waiting for the first bell, staring across the ring at my foe, or in this case staring way up miles into the sky at the white hard-rock summit, the Giant of Provence silently looking back down on me. I thought back to Dr Barr referring to me as his 1000/1 shot and I smiled and wondered what odds he would have given me to be stood here now, 364 days later, or the odds of me actually achieving my goal and cycling up that mighty mass of volcanic rock in the morning, a year to the day after my heart-blip.

Who knows and does it really matter? Of course not. I was there and I would make it or die trying, my stubborn mentality had kicked in, I was fired up. I gave the summit one more long hard stare.

'I'll see you tomorrow,' I said to myself and turned and drove back the same route. I was glad I had made the effort to recon the route; it took the pressure off in some ways and gave me the opportunity to psychologically prepare for the morning. It was going to be a very big day.

There was a hive of activity on returning to the house, bikes all checked over, made ready for the morning, they were good to go. Bottles were filled with water and put to freeze overnight, kit was laid out ready. The plan was to set off by eight in the hope of reaching the summit of Ventoux before the heat of midday. Preparations complete, we gathered for one final drink before some much-needed rest. One by one the boys trooped off to bed leaving just Kelly and me sat talking. She was now very unsure about attempting the ride up Ventoux. I think the reality of the climb now she had seen it close up had shaken her confidence, bearing in mind she was still a relative novice to road cycling despite her fitness which was more than good enough to get her up to the summit in my opinion. As long as she took care on the descent, she would be fine. As she went up to bed, she really wasn't sure.

I said, 'there is no pressure Kelly see how you feel in the morning, I will give you a knock about half six.' We gave each other a hug and wished each other good night.

I was now sat alone. The house was silent and darkness had fallen but, before turning in, I stepped outside and took one final look up at Mont Ventoux. She cast a huge black outline, the aircraft-warning light on the summit like a star shining in the night sky.

I reflected on the whole journey, from coming around out of the coma to standing here right now. It had been a hell of a journey with many highs and lows, life-changing for me in many ways. I had learned so much about myself. I had gained so much too and the positives out-weighed the negatives. Proud of everything I had overcome to get there, I couldn't have made it without the help and support of a whole host of people. I still felt I had the easiest part to play in all of this and was deeply humbled by the time and effort all these people had invested in me. I felt I owed it to each and every one of them as well as myself to stand on that summit tomorrow and say 'we made it' and I believed that I could. There was the toughest ride of my life standing between me and that moment, I truly felt like I had a date with destiny when dawn would come calling. The whole year had been about this, it was almost time; all the fears, doubts, hopes, dreams, were about to be answered one way or another.

It had been a good year.

12

The Climb

9th June 2014

It was the 9th June 2014, a year to the day since my heart blip and where had the year gone? What had seemed at times like a long journey to get to this day, now felt like the blink of an eye. I hadn't slept much but this was normal. I was up around 5.30 am, the sun shining brightly, skies crystal clear and beautiful blue, hardly a breath of wind, a perfect day for the ride. Already warm as I stepped into the garden, stretching, massaged by the sun, a few lengths of the pool later I was feeling relaxed and generally in good shape for the ride to come. By 6 am I was sat with a coffee, my usual pre-ride bowl of porridge, bananas, honey and the compulsory pint of water although this morning I made an exception and had two. Hey it was my 1st birthday. I felt good, like a kid on Christmas morning, I couldn't wait to get at the Ventoux. I sat and enjoyed my moment of peace and serenity in the early morning sun, life was good. Breakfast done and squared away, I gave the bikes one final check over although they didn't need it, it was more for my own peace of mind. At 6.30 am I made my way quietly upstairs to Kelly's room and opened the door; she was already awake sat up in bed.

Knowing her as any father knows his daughters, I could tell instantly by the look on her face what her decision was about attempting to ride up Ventoux. I did my best to try talking her round and boost her confidence by telling her I truly believed she was more than capable of making it and she would be ok, but I could feel she wasn't comfortable about things so didn't push it. We sat and talked it through for a while and it was ok although we were both a little disappointed. She had worked hard, I would have loved her to ride with me, but still, she was here, she had helped and supported me so much. There would be more cycling to come that week to enjoy and ride together, we were good.

The boys were all up by now so Kelly got up and came down and we all sat around chatting while they had breakfast. The mood was good. Stig feeling a bit nervous and, again, we had the conversation about no one being left behind. He would be fine; I had no doubts and a few pre-ride nerves were understandable. The frozen bottles pulled from the freezer and loaded into the bottle cages on the bikes, all kitted up, we were almost ready to go. Kelly gathered us together taking some pictures then we shared a big old bear hug and she wished me good luck. We looked forward to our post-Mont-Ventoux-conquering meal together later that evening. She stood and waved us off.

It was show time. The clicks of the cleats on our cycling shoes broke the morning silence as we locked into the pedals, rolling away down the hill. We were underway at last. The culmination of all the training, hard work over the last twelve months was about to be put to the test. Briefly I looked up towards the Giant of Provence - destiny was calling me. My heart pounding, finally I was cycling towards the Mont Ventoux.

Big George and Paul lead the way down through Pernes Les Fontain with Digger, Stig just behind; I was bringing up the rear. The wonderful smells from the early-morning bake filled the air as we rolled past the local patisserie. Freshly baked bread, croissants and brewing coffee has to be one of the finest smells in the world. Swinging right out of town towards Carpentras, rolling along, just turning the legs gently and stretching out.

The first ten miles to Bedoin would be used as a warm-up really, nothing strenuous so as to waist no precious energy, which would be needed on the brutal, unforgiving climb to come. The heat was building already despite it being early, still only a little after eight. The heat was beginning to bear down on our backs. I was sweating a lot yet hardly working at all. As I rolled through Carpentras towards the sprawling vineyards and Bedoin beyond, I had already gone through two thirds of one of the two bottles I carry on the bike. Clearly the heat was going to play a huge part. Taking on enough fluids is critical to a cyclist and this was magnified that day given the heat and severity of the climb.

The road ramped up to around 7% for a couple of miles as we passed through one of the many beautiful vineyards in the area. An early test of the legs; I was comfortable in all honesty, not fazed at all. The road surface helped - unlike the appalling tarmac I was used to cycling on back home, this was smooth, not a pothole in sight, perfectly laid, a true pleasure to cycle on. I found this to be the case every inch of the ride. France in general, and particularly the deep south, is an amazing place to cycle.

Paul and Big George had pushed on a bit climbing up through the vineyards; I had ridden up with Digger; Stig was rolling along nice and steady. I thought he was pedaling well although he did seem a little on edge. Just outside of Bedoin there was a road island with a big stone monument with silver letters reading 'Mont Ventoux' and, as it was early and having the road virtually to ourselves, we stopped for a photo. Our water had taken a big hit, it was decided we would stop on reaching Bedoin now only a mile away and refill with fresh water from the fridges and drink our fill, before starting the climb itself. There was a market selling wonderful local produce in full swing as we rolled into town. We found chilled water, refilled the bottles and stood in the shade drinking our fill. 35 degrees and climbing we all had a good sweat on by now; Stig looked as though someone had thrown a bucket of water over him. I hadn't realized until now just how hard he had worked to get here to Bedoin, I wasn't concerned but I knew it was going to be a hard struggle for him from here on in. Finishing our drinks, shaking hands we wished each other good luck, rolling through town taking the famous right-hand-turn sign posted 'Mont Ventoux, sommet 21 km'. What it should say in my opinion is '21 km of pain and suffering'. We cheered as our battle with the mighty Ventoux began. Now we were climbing.

Full of anticipation I couldn't help but smile as the road ramped up straight away on leaving Bedoin. The first 5 km approximately up to Saint-Esteve are the kindest part of the mountain to a cyclist, average gradient between 5% and 6%, enough to work you but not enough to hurt you if you understand what I mean. Quite a number of cyclists were sharing the mountain. Apparently the Dutch military had a charity ride that day, good company indeed, nice bunch of guys. There were cyclists from all over the world. Such is the mythical fame of Mont Ventoux, it is a mecca for cyclists. It is quite surreal to think, if you can get there with your bike, you can ride the slopes where the toughest bike race on earth takes place and here I was living the dream. For the non-cyclists amongst you, it's like having a kick about at Wembley, playing rugby at Twickenham, tennis on centre court Wimbledon or cricket at Lords. As a cyclist it doesn't get much better than this.

Temperatures were soaring, 38 degrees, baking heat bouncing back off the wonderfully smooth tarmac below the fresh rubber of my new tires. Feeling the heat on my legs and stomach, my back taking the full force of the sun beating down on me, boy was I ever glad for the white shirts now. Riding as a group through the early kilometres Big George and Paul had taken up position riding on the front, clearly very strong, riding well within themselves at this stage, chatting away, laughing and joking, it was good to see. Digger had settled into his machine-like rhythm. I had seen this many times. His ability to keep going, his power of endurance, would carry him to the summit, I had no doubts. Stig was plugging away at the tail end, working hard and now showing a few early signs of the pain and suffering that would follow.

I was feeling good. The time and distance in the saddle were paying dividends as I had hoped they would. I had pushed myself to near destruction over the last year in order to feel as comfortable as I did now.

I had been rotating round, trying my best to have a chat with all the boys. Paul would occasionally launch away as only he could, pulling over a few hundred metres ahead and taking photos of us as we approached him then tagging back on. Big George was turning away nice and easy, riding well. The last km on the approach to Saint-Esteve Stig had fallen behind by only maybe a hundred metres, but that can feel like a mile if you're the one losing touch. I dropped back to him and rode alongside. He was indeed beginning to suffer. I didn't say as much but I knew he was going to have to dig deep, to the very bottom of his resolve, die a thousand deaths to make it to the summit from there. I think he knew it too. He wasn't going to be left behind, he wasn't going to fail; I wouldn't let that happen. If I had to push him up I would gladly do it, but one way or another we were all going to make it as I had promised him.

Pulling up at Saint-Esteve, taking a couple of min to gather our thoughts, taking stock of the water situation which we were consuming at an astonishing rate. It was 38 degrees by then with very little wind, the air becoming thinner and with increasing altitude it felt much hotter. Mont Ventoux can be roughly split in to three sections, the first of which we had covered. This had been the warm-up compared to the brutal forest section from Saint-Esteve, our current position, to Chalet Reynard, approximately 9.5km further up the mountain. The trees would provide a welcome shade from the direct impact of the baking sun, but the Ventoux plays a brutal game of cloak-and-dagger with you. She gives you shade but increases the gradient on that section to an average 10% with short hits of 12% to break your legs and pull your lungs out. I had ridden gradients like this before, casting my mind back to Jiggers Bank, Happy Valley and Cadair Idris, yes they had been similar but only for a few hundred metres at a time; this was 9.5 km. My cycling brain found it hard to accept: how could a road be so steep for so long? The fact remained - it was.

A brief team-talk of sorts took place. It was clear that from there on it would be difficult to ride as a group. It is hard to climb for long periods at someone else's pace and Big George and Paul were free and easy, comfortable riding together, so they would carry on ahead. Digger was happy settling into his own rhythm to grind his way up the torturous slopes - and I had made my decision to ride with Stig, despite him wishing me to carry on, not wanting to hold me back and spoil my ride. He didn't succeed because I was happy to ride with him. As we left Saint-Esteve, the unforgiving forest section soon put our group to the sword, splitting us quite quickly. I watched Paul and Big George pull away up into the distance, pedaling so strong. They looked good on it to. Digger pulled out a good few hundred metres and I could see him now and again as I looked up.

My whole approach to climbing the Ventoux now changed. I hope he doesn't mind me saying, but Stig, struggling big time, was indeed beginning to die the thousand deaths I always knew he would at some point. Suffering like a dog, I talked to him constantly trying to reassure him he would make it. He was strong enough.

'Just focus, don't look to far up the road. Keep em turning, mate, nice and easy, we'll be ok.'

I don't know if any of my words helped. When you're deep in the red zone as Stig now was, from my own experience you ride in a daze, almost unable to comprehend anything but the ten feet of tarmac in front of you and the world of pain your body is in. With this mindset, we plugged away one pedal stroke after the other.

I found it quite amazing how my body quickly adjusted to cycling on such steep gradients for so long. Breathing nicely, feeling comfortable. Don't get me wrong, it was hard yakka. There is no getting away from the fact that this mountain is cruel, so unforgiving, no let up or rest even for a second. It hurts you, puts you firmly in the hurt locker and keeps you there, legs burning constantly as the lactic acid builds up and fatigue sets in. There is no escape for mile after mile. The 'god of evil' as the locals call Ventoux chips away at your physical strength and hammers your psychological resolve, trying to crack you, willing you to stop and pull over, or, that fate worse than death in my opinion, to get off and push. Just no with a capital no! I have said this many times and I will stand by it here in black and white, I have never once got off my bike and pushed it up a climb; I would die first. Inevitably that day will come but I hope not for many years. When it does, I will hang up my wheels, invest in some new walking boots take up walking and never ride a bike again. I simply could not bear it.

For all the suffering and hurt the Ventoux bestows on you, she blesses you with amazing scenery. It's such a beautiful place to ride a bike, walk, or anything else that takes your fancy. Through the trees you see the valley way down below and already we had climbed higher than some of the other mountains in the area. The smell of the pines, the pure clean air, it was a pleasure to be there despite the pain. Rounding a bend, the clues that Chalet Reynard was now only a few kilometres away were painted on the road in front of us. It's a tradition in cycle racing that the fans paint the names of their idols and the greats of our sport on the roads on the upper reaches of the famous tour climbs such as the Ventoux. I had seen them many times over the years on tv watching the Tour de France, now I was riding over them myself, just as the giants of the road had done themselves in full view of the cycling world on their way to glory long before me. I felt honored to share the same tarmac as those great riders. To name but a few, I saw that day: Pantani & Armstrong (who could forget their epic battle up Ventoux), Cavendish, Virenque and Vockler, I spotted, my own personal favorite, Merckx. His name still painted in all its splendor all those years after his racing days ended. Even the great Eddy Merckx suffered like a dog on those slopes. I believe it was the 1970 tour he rode so hard up the Ventoux he virtually collapsed as he crossed the line. We were suffering in the best of company.

The heat of the mid-morning sun began to find its way on to our backs once more as the much-appreciated shade of the trees subsided, with the forest thinning out due to the altitude and the thin air. We could see Chalet Reynard up ahead just under a kilometer away.

Stig was in a world of hurt. I was so impressed by his willingness to suffer and keep on grinding it out. The boys had all arrived at Reynard a good few minutes earlier, buying chilled water from the fridges, and we drank the cooling, soothing water. It was hard not to drink too much too quickly such was our thirst and the need to cool down. The heat was stifling, you could feel the air so much thinner at this altitude, a new experience to me. We sat a few minutes in the shade of an umbrella to give Stig a chance to recover and regroup; he had worked so hard to get this far. The summit was approximately 6 km from here and we would all just ride our own pace: the plan - to meet 1.5 km from the top at the Tommy Simpson memorial. The cyclists amongst you will know the significance, for the non-cyclists, Tommy Simpson was a British professional cyclist who paid the ultimate price of his life whilst battling his way up the mighty Ventoux in the 1967 Le Tour. His monument stands at the point on the climb where he finally succumbed to the pain, suffering and demands of pro-cycling. May the wind be forever at your back, sir.

The views from Chalet Reynard are quite spectacular. As far as the eye can see are rolling fields, valleys, mountains, wonderful colors of purple, yellow, green and gold far below. Setting off once again, the heat was overwhelming and I felt as though I was being pushed into the floor. Big George and Paul soon pulled away by quite a distance. They were still riding very strong, I was impressed by the seemingly light work they had made of this iconic climb. Digger was grinding away halfway between them and myself, with Stig locked in his own personal battle alongside me. This third section of the Ventoux was, for me, the toughest part although the gradient drops slightly to an average of around 8% with a few nasty short kicks of 10% and 12% here and there. It's the psychological impact that makes it so hard those last 6 km. Once past Chalet Reynard nothing grows because the altitude is too high, not a tree, not a single blade of grass. The whole vast area is bare, white, weather-battered, barren rock. It has been likened to the surface of the moon in many books I have read. Now there in that place, I could see why. The weather station stands tall on the summit like a beacon and it cruelly deceives you into thinking you're almost there, but you're not. 6 km of leg breaking, heart-bursting punishment still has to be covered; you feel you're getting nowhere as every inch is identical to the inch before, it's horrid.

Pushing on in that relentless heat, I kept continually talking to Stig, trying to encourage him to keep going.

'Just keep turning your legs, mate, nice and steady, you're doing well.'

Did it help? I don't know in truth. He was suffering badly but I could see in his face that he was determined to make it. It's fair to say I have never witnessed anyone, to this day, dig so deep, suffer and soak up the pain the way Stig did that day, if there had been a prize for 'ride of the day' he would have won it with ease. In the months leading up to the Ventoux there had been trials and tribulations in Stig's life. We talked about a lot of these things on our toil up the mountain. He had been through a lot and was indeed battling his own demons that day as was I, for different reasons maybe. We shared our motivation to make the summit. It is not my place to tell his story but I will say this: I have the upmost respect for the way he dug deep and endured when many would have quit. It was an honour to share the road and climb with him, Chapeaux Stig, Chapeaux indeed.

Gathering at the Tommy Simpson memorial we shared a few nice moments altogether, took on some water and the last of our snacks in preparation to fuel the last 1.5km to the summit. A couple of Dutch cyclists had stopped to see the memorial also, the opportunity for a rare picture of us altogether was taken and what better place to do it than there. I felt so proud of all the boys. It was quite surreal: here we were altogether and our Tommy for company, sat on the Ventoux. I had a chat with Big George. He had loved the ride so far and felt comfortable doing it, testament to all the long hours and hard miles he had put in to get there. It showed too, he was strong and took the Ventoux with ease and, if I am honest, it was an awesome ride on his part, he made it look easy, I was proud of him and his achievements. I spoke with Paul too, at that point I urged him to stick his big ring on and ride at full gas the last 1.5 km.

'We'll probably never be here again, mate. Just have a go, give it the full beans.'

Grinning at me, I could see in his face he was itching to have a go and test himself

Digger was typical Digger: strong, powerful, machine-like in his rhythm from way back down in Bedoin, so impressive, his powers of stamina and endurance were simply relentless, a top ride indeed by a top man.

A final shake of hands as we left our Tommy behind and the last push to the summit, to achieving the crazy unthinkable goal that I had set myself a year ago, was underway. Three very long, straight sections of road with a hair-pin bend at each, average gradient 9%, was now all that stood between me and achieving what I had set out to do. I could see Paul already some 400 metres ahead, churning away in his monster gears on the big ring, powering along, passing every other cyclist, of which there were many, with ease. There were some very exceptional cyclists riding the Ventoux that day but our Paul was by far and away the strongest. He made it look easy and then some. I smiled as I watched him smash his way up. As a kid Paul had all the talent and potential in the world and this was a clear glimpse of what might have been, a truly awesome display of climbing by a truly awesome cyclist. It was a pleasure for me to sit tapping away and see it.

I spotted Big George way up ahead with his instantly recognizable bolt-upright climbing style, hands gently resting on the tops, powering along at a good pace. He was showing a good many how to do it. Fit and strong, a far cry from the day we could barely turn our granny gears up past the donkey sanctuary on a twenty miler. I recall thinking 'go on Big George give it em' and he did. Six hundred metres to go, which doesn't sound far, but on that gradient it was still a fair distance and chunk of time, Stig was digging in so deep now but he would make it and I had kept my word and ridden with him. And I was happy doing it because, from my position, I had been able to watch all the boys ride their hearts out up the mighty Ventoux. They had come to this place to ride for me and with me, but each also had his own personal battles to overcome to reach the summit.

I was proud of them all; it was a huge effort. I hope they all laid their ghosts to rest and now treasure the memories of the epic ride each one of them put in that day.

Big George, Paul and Digger were stood applauding with big smiles on their faces, shouting encouragement as Stig and I made our way around the last hair-pin bend. Fifty metres to the official finishing line - the whole of the last year had been about this moment and now the emotion of the day and the build-up to it hit me like a freight train. I was exhausted; I hadn't realized this until that moment, not so much physically, don't get me wrong my legs were heavy and I could feel every one of the 21 km and 6273 ft I had climbed from Bedoin in that relentless 38 degrees heat, but psychologically I was exhausted. The pressure I had felt the last year, at first to simply survive then to get moving and build up to getting back on the bike, the training the ups and downs along the way, the journey to get here, the ride itself, all that pressure. As I rolled across the finishing line, I felt it all lift off my shoulders and float away on the mistral wind.

Rolling to a stop, Stig alongside me, we went in to one of those proper big old bear-hug moments. It was all quite emotional to be honest; he thanked me for getting him up there. I was deeply moved, in truth and on reflection, my efforts to help Stig that day helped me in equal quantity; they took my mind off my own suffering and pain. I hadn't noticed how much the climb had taken out of me because my focus had been on Stig and he had helped me as much as I had helped him, I have no doubt about it. The boys found us blubbering away then handshakes all round. It was a special moment for me and I couldn't have done it without those good friends of mine. They had done me proud every one of them; I will always be in their debt and forever grateful for their support.

We spent a while up on the summit taking pictures and admiring the view. The altitude was such that the horizon was no longer flat and the curvature of the earth was visible I was amazed by this. To be able to look down on the clouds from a good distance above them was breathtaking in every sense of the word, given the ride I had taken on to get there. I sat a while looking out across the mountains, thinking back to the days I lay in hospital, not really able to grasp the severity of my condition. The darkest hours of my life in the ICU, bang on the limits of my pain threshold, unable to move. My heroic yet feeble and pathetic attempts to walk but a few metres, dragging all the monitors and equipment behind me. Did I truly believe back then I would live to see this day? Honest answer: no. The early days were about surviving one day at a time and each sunrise was another box ticked. When the idea of riding something big, something special on the first anniversary of my heart blip was born, that's when the belief came. I have this kind of moto if you like: 'believe you can'. I am a great believer that you can achieve anything you want to in this life, you just got to want it bad enough and believe you can. We all have dark days and rough times, those days when you want to quit, sit down and cry and that's ok, there is nothing wrong in that, and certainly no shame, in my opinion. I have been there.

I had wanted to quit and questioned myself many times along my journey but I am lucky, and I do mean this in the best possible way: I am lucky that I have a big scar down the front of my chest that reminds me I have a second chance at this crazy life. I owe it to so many wonderful people who worked so hard to save me, got me back on my feet and then on the bike, cared for me, supported me, tolerated my infernal self-destructive attitude, taught me how to change, adapt and overcome. I would not have been sat there a year to the day later in that high and mighty place without them. Yes, indeed I owed so many so much and I owe it to myself to try and do those things for as long as I can. Whatever life throws at you, just pick yourself up, dust yourself down and go again. It's not a practice; we get one shot at this. I have been fortunate, very fortunate. I hope in some small way that this crazy journey of mine may give a little inspiration and motivation to some of you. You don't have to cycle a mountain, it doesn't matter what you do. Set yourself a goal, focus on it, and, above all else, just believe in yourself, 'believe you can'

I said 'thank you' in my mind to those closest to me, my family, friends, those who had saved me and God himself. I had never sat this close to the big man upstairs, and it felt appropriate somehow as I had asked for help on many occasions during the long journey that bought me to Mont Ventoux. I had put my faith on the line more than once but I was sat there now on the summit. I had made it and had my questions been answered. You decide.

A last look from the summit, I smiled, I really did feel as though I was stood on top of the world physically and psychologically. The weight now lifted from my shoulders, I could have floated back down. The plan was to roll the 6 km down to Chalet Reynard, stop for some nice chilled water and refill our bottles once again. The descent was such a reward. Paul lead the way and I was tucked in behind, the views were amazing, the speed incredible on those long, steep drops, the rush of air so welcome, cooling me down in the blistering heat. It was a lovely roll down.

Bottles refilled, we sat around a large table drinking beautiful iced water, the decision made to refrain from a drink until our celebration meal planned for later that evening. The boys surprised me with a momento, they had bought me - a Mont Ventoux cycling shirt form Chalet Reynard, I was deeply touched. It meant a lot to me. In summertime I give it an outing now and again and it never fails to make me smile and take me back to that moment we were altogether laughing, joking, enjoying our achievement We had toiled and suffered together but we had made it. For myself, I was elated beyond any words I can write. The feeling I had at that moment will stay with me always. It was the equal and exact opposite to how I felt a year earlier. My goal achieved, I was complete again in my mind. I had survived and comeback from the brink, I had locked horns with the Giant of Provence, I had climbed the Mont Ventoux.

13

Paying tribute

I was in two minds whether or not to add this afterword, but I feel it is as big a part of this journey as anything that happened before it. As we rolled away from Chalet Reynard bearing left towards the town of Saulte, my spirits could not have been better. I was in high ascendency of relief and achievement, rolling along in the midday sun, carefree and easy, happy in my own skin once more. I had turned the page on an epic year and life was good. I was very much looking forward to our planned stop for lunch in Saulte and to seeing Kelly later and I knew she would be so excited and pleased for me and the boys.

My thoughts were already planning two years ahead. The following year, on the 9th June, my intention was to return to France and climb the Col du Tourmalet, a mighty and famous tour-climb mountain, the scene of many classic Tour de France battles over the years, an epic climb. The year after that I would climb the Alpe du Huez, arguably the most famous and celebrated tour climb of them all, with its beautifully scenic and technical twenty-one hair-pin bends. Of course, there are many more such climbs but these, for me, along with the Ventoux, were my three big goals. One down two to go. Then I would take it from there. I was filled with excitement, my passion for the sport I love so much fully reignited. The inner chimp was happy and finally at peace deep down within me - for now at least.

I had, for some reason and I don't know why, maybe it was an omen of some kind, whilst climbing to the summit earlier, recalled a quote written by the French philosopher Rolland Barthes. He had written, 'the Ventoux is a god of evil to which sacrifices must be made, it never forgives weakness and extracts an unfair tribute of suffering'. Now, I am quite superstitious, as are most cyclists and soon those mythical superstitions of the Ventoux were utterly confirmed. Thankfully in my opinion, I had taken up position at the front of our group to lead us back down the 21 km off the mountain, ten of which were now safely behind us. Rolling along nice and easy enjoying the sunshine and spectacular views without a care in the world, a left-hand sweeping hairpin bend came into view. I positioned myself to roll smoothly round and through, banked over on a good line, even thinking what a pleasure it was. Then out of nowhere came the sacrifice and indeed tribute it seemed I was destined to pay this god of evil. A motorcycle travelling in the opposite direction had chosen a poor line through the bend, carrying it over onto my side of the road on a direct collision course with me. I had absolutely nowhere to go, no time to react, the inevitable crash happened and, in the blink of an eye, everything had changed.

I heard a loud bang and a sickening crack and saw a flash of blinding light which was more than likely the sun, and was sent spinning by the impact. I seemed to be air born for an eternity. Eventually the sky gave way to a face-full of tarmac. Dazed and in a lot of pain, blood was streaming from my mouth and arm and all over my hands. Instantly I put my right hand inside my shirt to feel the sternum; thank God it had held up, the blood wasn't coming from there. I tried to feel and count my teeth and thankfully they had all survived but blood was pouring from the deep wound on my inner lip and chin where I had face-planted the road. My head was spinning, the helmet was trashed but had done its job well, as was confirmed by the surgeon who would later examine what remained of it, saying, 'saved your life no question about it'.

Boy, I was in some pain. My back, hip, hands were on fire as most of the skin had been scrapped off them by the red-hot tarmac. Then the cherry on the cake, as I looked trying my best to do an all over body check whilst still lay in the road, the root cause of my pain and bleeding became obvious to me. Halfway up my left arm and the full width of it was a deep wound, the muscle and bone were sticking out nicely; my wrist and elbow were also clearly broken. The boys carried me to the side of the road to some shade. Tribute had been paid, I guess, to the god of evil. As destiny would have it, the mighty Mont Ventoux had had the last word. I was just glad it was me and none of the others. I say this hand on heart: in that moment all I had achieved had gone. No matter how many times I try to convince myself differently, to this day I do not feel as though I did what I went there to do. Yes, I climbed the mountain but being bought off it in an ambulance was not part of the deal. It burns and eats away at my very soul deep inside me. I know me better than anyone and it's a fact that unless I return to that god-forsaken, baking rock again someday and finish what I started, I will never have that inner peace I so briefly enjoyed sat on the summit and drinking ice water at Chalet Reynard with the boys. Cycling can be so very cruel.

So, fate would have it I would spend the first anniversary of my heart blip, the 9th June 2014, the same way I had done a year earlier: in solitary in the back of an ambulance although at least this time I was conscious. Reconstructive surgery of my left arm with all its pins, plates, screws, skin grafts and many stitches were added to my fine collection, replacing what was intended to be a celebration meal. I was heartbroken, physically battered again and psychologically the scars would run very deep - I carry them badly to this day. This was not the ending I had imagined. Would I recover and get back on the bike to chase my goals once more; time will tell, I guess. You can bet your butt I would give it all my best shot, all or nothing as always, soak up the pain, John boy. What choice did I have? none at all. I had come a full circle. It was that time again where I had to pick myself up, dust myself off, and go again. After all there were more mountains to climb, goals to achieve, and indeed my second chance at this crazy life to live. I was down again but not out, I was ok, I would bounce back. I just had to take a deep breath and live by my own philosophy: 'believe you can'.

46607030R00110

Printed in Poland
by Amazon Fulfillment
Poland Sp. z o.o., Wrocław